By the same author:

Some We Loved
Told with a Drum
Light Over Ruby Street
Any Number Can Play
We Are the Robbers
If You Lived Here
The Wonderful World of Cooking

MY LIFE
ON
EARTH

by Edward Harris Heth

illustrations by Edwin Schmidt

Wisconsin Tales and Trails, Incorporated,
Madison, Wisconsin 1973

Printed by Litho Productions, Incorporated,
Madison, Wisconsin.

For Marie and Ernst Wallau

CONTENTS

1. Up the Road ... 1
2. Master Builder ... 17
3. The Willow Road and the Yokel ... 35
4. The Very Tired Veery ... 48
5. To Right and Left ... 53
6. And Neighbors in the Night ... 71
7. The Roots ... 79
8. The Dill Crock ... 92
9. The Waukesha Mail-Pouch Robbery ... 102
10. The First Leaf ... 116
11. Brief Stay ... 131
12. Land to Give Away ... 143
13. The Postals and the Turkey ... 152
14. Wine from These Grapes ... 165
15. Reign's End ... 178
16. Pyramid Builders ... 193

17. *Anniversary*   211

18. *The Closing Seasons*   223

19. *More Magi*   238

20. *Waldeen*   243

1

Up the Road

YOU might as well, right off, meet my new friends, the Litten sisters. I call them new, though they are old and tried friends now. But they were new when this story begins.

It is a wrench for a man to leave New York City, especially when his love for that city has been fierce and expectant, and take up life again in an alien, rural countryside. It is an even greater wrench when the move is not voluntary, but a kind of senseless accident. A man, faced with this peculiar loneliness of being where he doesn't want to be, is apt to find himself driving along the narrow, twisting country roads, day or night, alone, brooding about the tricks life can play. In such a mood, he wants no neighbors. He will not even recognize they live near him. He is most at ease driving along those roads alone.

But gradually one of the roads became more favored than the others. It took more than a year to find it. But soon I began to travel it with a sense of destiny, for it led to the house where the Littens lived. Even, in time, the brooding turned to expectation. Certainly traveling that road was never less than an ad-

venture, when I had begun to think I would never find adventure again—it was only that this was another kind, one I had forgotten about during the past decade of full, breathless New York years. Then before too long the expectation became wonder. I would find that an irresistible force had drawn me along that road again and set me down in front of the trim red house, honking the horn of my car and waiting to see from what strange place—the abandoned corn crib, from behind a golden bell bush, or from underneath their '29 Essex—Miss Millie or Miss Carrie Litten would emerge.

They are two remarkable women and very wise, in their sixties, though their exact age or sequence I don't know since each, when alone with me, refers to the other as her elder sister. They have an Old Testament talent for disaster. They play a good game of canasta, even though sometimes they confuse it with bridge and bid grand slams, and play them. What's more, make them. Sometimes Carrie will ask Millie how her cold is, when Carrie's the one sniffling, but that hardly matters since Millie obligingly swallows a cold pill then.

They are, too, spectacular cooks. Their recipe (though they call it a receipt) for duck with sauerkraut stuffing is famous in our county from Muckwonago to Okauchee, and once I even made the mistake of trying to get it from them. It was the duck, for that matter, that started me up their special road the first time.

In those days—the first year of despair and anger—I did not yet know what giving a country party really meant. The New York parties, the ones I couldn't go to any more, though they were only that hurried apartment variety, with the host rushing out for a bottle of whisky and a bag of pretzels, were the only kind that seemed to matter; it was all part of what I had lost.

Country parties are of another kind, entailing sacrifice and long cheerful occupation. Aunt Dell wears herself to a frazzle for several days making Krumkaka for her son Tom's birthday, or a dozen ladies from Jerusalem Church rise at five in the morning to start basting their crackling, golden pork loin roasts and creaming tubs of potatoes in a satiny sauce with tiny onions for the church supper that evening. Or Walter Cwym, who runs the vegetable stand in Genesee, will spend a week in September mashing his wormy apples in a hand press against the winter night when you might come over for some applejack with him in his kitchen.

Wasted labor, it seemed to me. I did not know what cheer and comfort there was in it. Those things, I had still to learn. For a year I had tried to keep neighbors from bothering me. Until, in the second spring, Bud Devere dropped by.

He was young and burly, and grinned when I opened the door. "The folks in the village thought you might want to drop in at the church supper tonight," he said. "Thought you might want to start getting acquainted."

I shook my head. I had things to do, I said.

"Hell," Bud grinned. "You got to come off it sometime." He had an easygoing way of making me seem not quite human, but that he didn't really mind. He flung a cigarette into the pillar roses. "Anyway, the Littens are bringing duck." He said it conclusively, and took my arm. "For Christ's sake, fella, come along."

But what he meant was that no man in his senses walked in the opposite direction from the Littens' duck. I felt a sudden whiff of the spring evening air blow into my nostrils as he led me toward his car—it was the first touch of mildness I had sensed in the air that year.

Miss Millie and Miss Carrie had fixed their duck lovingly, working all day in their kitchen with the shades down, I learned later, and delivering it at six o'clock sharp to the basement of the church in their Essex, also with *its* shades down. They are well-beloved sights around our countryside, often touring in their well-kept Essex on rainy days as well as fair, Millie at the wheel, though she is the frailer of the two and quite thin, while Carrie, plump and of a rosy cast, rides in the back seat like a visiting sovereign.

The secret of their duck was well worth guarding, the famous stuffing rich with diced salt pork, caraway seed, apples, chopped sauerkraut, and some other mysterious ingredient—burnt brown sugar, brandy? All through the supper Carrie and Millie sat in silence, not at the long crowded tables, but on slatted wooden chairs to one side of the basement, looking like high priestesses, their eyes narrowed and fixed on the gobbling faces, as if fearful they might detect in a sudden glance of elation the horrible news that to someone there had been revealed what Aunt Dell, my neighbor to the south, calls the secret "ingrediment." But no such revelation lit any face. At seven prompt the Littens arose, collected their pans, and started home.

On the way out they passed behind my chair. "That's the man lives up on the hill. Moved out here a year ago," Millie said, as if I were invisible.

Carrie nodded to me, and with a shy smile headed toward the vestibule. There was a slight confusion, because they got into each other's coat by mistake, which involved setting down their pans again, switching coats, then re-collecting their pans, before they disappeared out to their waiting Essex.

*   *   *

But on the next evening, I started out again to travel alone over the long, silent roads. I was eager to escape the house— Bud Devere, after the church supper the night before, had hinted he might be dropping up. For months I had been wanting nothing but to leave Wisconsin and return to New York, but each time I thought I had pried that door open, it slammed shut again—shaky health, lack of money, a surprising lack of interest when I wrote old acquaintances for a job, and at last, most stunningly of all, my mother's sudden sickness and death. Now I did not want that door opened from the other side by neighbors or new friends.

I left my own house to avoid Bud Devere. I drove down the dark road slowly, having no place special to go, not wanting to go any place but back home to West Seventy-third Street, near Verdi Square, near Central Park, near all the New York noise and passing, unknown faces and quick sounds of laughter coming from no place in particular, from behind a drawn window shade, perhaps, or from inside a neon-lighted bar. I let the car drive itself, thinking my bitter, usual thoughts: if only the funny trick hadn't happened, if the monstrous joke had never begun. . . .

Too, I kept needling myself as I crawled along the road, if I had gone to the doctor in time, if I hadn't kept putting it off, as all New Yorkers do, because there isn't time to worry about things like health or peace of mind, then perhaps the big joke might never have come off. For breaking health—only a dizziness at first as I laid out some new advertising scheme before a dour-eyed client, or an unexpected desire to scream at this same client—had been the first link in the chain that now kept me fettered in the countryside, as irrevocably as any steer fastened by a nose ring to a fence post.

Ernie Pollock, who owned our agency, would watch me thoughtfully. You'd better slow up, take a little time off, where's the race . . . ? Only, I reasoned in answer, after nearly ten years of fighting, of getting where, in some kind of confusion, you had come to believe you ought to be (since surely this was not the place you had wanted to reach when you first arrived in New York, suitcase, one hundred dollars, ambition, wild belief, in hand), it did not seem logical to take time off, to let new or younger men muscle their way into the private office that had at last become yours.

A tendency of the throat to constrict suddenly, a sense of dislocation behind my closed eyelids, shortness of breath as I climbed stairs, which made me take them twice as fast—these were the signs, I told myself now, that should have sent me pell-mell into the first doctor's office I passed. But doctors are tactless; they mention cold facts, like life or death. A later tendency to let work pile up, to snap at Ernie Pollock, to leave the office early for the bar at the New Weston. To the warnings behind such behavior I might have listened, too.

But earning big money had grown pleasant, living in New York was pleasant, success was pleasant. Wasn't all else folly? So one learns diabolically almost to woo the sleepless nights that finally come, let them come, they'll pass, come on, come on . . . until the nerves sever, the body collapses, the spirit breaks. And the heart with it.

*   *   *

These were my thoughts, black as the arms of trees overhead, as I found myself on the Littens' road. The car had stopped itself. Perhaps the sight of the Littens' house in itself encouraged me, painted bright red, pristine with white trim—every spring the two of them can be seen scaling its walls to put on a fresh coat—but before I knew why I did it I had left the car. I was knocking at their door, obeying their come-ins, and beginning to introduce myself.

But Millie interrupted me from her rocker. "Who else would you be?" A country greeting. I had the dim sensation of having come to some felicitous place. I had not felt it before, not even at the church supper one evening ago.

Carrie's greeting also was neighborly. "You look like you could use a little supper, couldn't you?"

"No, thanks. I had a big supper." In answer to their pitying smiles of doubt I enumerated two martinis, a rib roast, Yorkshire pudding, and a salad of dandelion shoots and young, wild, lemony sorrel sprouts from the meadow. I had read in some book that these were edible, and had gathered them to fill hours of boredom. I had tasted them, though, with pleased shock.

Carrie and Millie still looked at me dubiously, so I began to repeat the list, rib roast, pudding, salad. . . .

"Don't apologize," Carrie smiled, as if I had said shredded wheat. "We can always find something here, easy enough."

Even now, sometimes, I can't look at Millie and Carrie without remembering the women of Verdi Square. The Square is a half-acre triangle near my New York apartment, squalid as only city squares can be. The grass is soot-smothered. The benches are hard and unfriendly. The view, that should be expansive, is prison-like—there are only drugstores, squeezed-in delicatessens, bars, lunch counters, a close-faced, forbidding bank, to gaze at. The sky overhead is starless, neon-streaked.

And all around the three sides of Verdi Square shriek the cabs, trolleys, buses. But then the women of Verdi Square had no effect on my heart muscles. I loved New York, I longed to go back. I could hurry easily past those old women on hot summer nights, not seeing the trapped look in their eyes. They were not young any longer; they lived on my block or nearby blocks, and they came down from their rooms after sundown to try to find a thin thread of something to breathe on the crowded, impersonal Square. There are a half-dozen spindly trees there, with parched, misshapen leaves. The ladies must still be sitting beneath them on the hard benches, on hot fumey nights, palms upturned in their laps, hoping for a breath of air, for a neighbor to talk to, for a sign of life.

Now, years later, I try to imagine Millie and Carrie trapped on such a half-acre of earth under a dusty, lifeless, city night, instead of blooming lusty as milkweed stalks in their own wide countryside, and I know what a lucky exchange I too have made, though it took me years to learn it. I know the same thing, now, when I'm with Walter Cwym, Joe, Aunt Dell, Ed and Paulie Waldeen, Harry, Tom Dell, Bud Devere, Buck Fife and his parents and sisters. But learning to know all this is the story.

* * *

In any city, Millie and Carrie would have expired behind locked doors. They need space and barns and fences to pick grapes from, and stray dogs to alarm them, and neighbors to visit in their Essex, and gardens to plant—even if overimaginatively, as when they planted sweet corn and gourds in the same hole, training the gourds up the corn stalks—so they wouldn't have to bother building trellises, naturally.

That first evening when I disturbed them by knocking on their door, they had been taking their after-supper naps. They are the only country women I know who do not do their dishes until they feel like it. It is the kind of unshackled common sense they abound in.

There was about them a dozey warmth. In their laps were an array of artificial flowers, faded poppies and pansies, and peculiar limp pink things which could have once been lilacs. I don't know why, but each fall they carefully snip all the flowers off their summer hats, store the flowers *and* the hats in the same box in a cool dry place, as one might store gladioli bulbs, and next spring sew the flowers back on again. For winter they transfer to beaver caps, plus mackinaws, plus thick canvas mittens and an assortment of scarves—you are always disappointed not to find them lugging rifles. But spring is resurrection. Out come the carefully stored flowers to bloom again on their gray heads. The flowers strewn now in their laps looked as pretty as any spring beauties speckling a hillside.

Millie yawned, got up from her rocker, tossing the flowers aside as indifferently as she might a bunch of weeds, and started for their pantry. Her face is little and wizened, but it can expand in generosity when she has a neighbor to help or a friend to serve. "Well, if this man's starving we'd better fix him a bite." She spied a button dangling on my jacket. "Button needs mending," she said, and yanked it off, dropping it in their button box—but did nothing about sewing a new one on. "Heard about Carrie's polly?"

I shook my head, and Millie looked at Carrie expectantly.

"It's just this polly I dream about every night," Carrie explained.

I waited, and I think Carrie was disappointed that I did not look satisfied.

"Nothing," she said. "He sits on my shoulder every night. That's all. He's so friendly."

Millie was already in the kitchen boiling coffee, strong, delicious, clarified with an egg, and Carrie took a plate of homemade fry cakes from under the taffeta hoopskirt of a Colonial doll, such as people used to hide telephones under. The coffee was strong enough, the talk comfortable enough, to make me mention the duck with sauerkraut stuffing. I wondered aloud what was in it.

Miss Millie turned to me in a paroxysm of helpfulness. She eyed me brightly. "Must have a slice of banana pie," she answered, and moved swiftly again toward the voluminous-skirted telephone doll.

We ate banana pie—or I did, while they watched sharply, nodding when I swallowed the last bite as if a mission had been accomplished. Millie had had other things on her mind when she baked the pie and put wild plum jam in by mistake, but since Carrie had been thinking of something else when she mixed the batter and made gingerbread instead, it didn't matter. It was a beautiful cake. I ate my large piece, and Carrie urged me to have more banana pie, and perhaps my answer sounded addled.

For Millie turned to me hesitantly. They are, after all, extremely openhanded women. Later I learned they love having visitors (and visiting), and, like Orientals, will turn over their home and possessions to the first one who asks for them. "You asked about the duck stuffing receipt?"

At which moment Miss Carrie went off into triumphant girlish laughter. "But I *didn't* say it was a duck. It's a polly."

Millie also broke into speckles of laughter. These were no defeated, sullen women from Verdi Square. I laughed with them, not sure at what, and then said I had better be leaving, but Carrie quickly trapped me by refilling my cup before I could rise from my chair. Carrie is slightly bosomy and moves with a bounce, and somehow gives the impression that she is wearing tennis sneaks. I wasn't even surprised, later, to see she was wearing them.

But as my coffee cup emptied again, Millie became more thoughtful. I think responsibilities weigh harder on Millie than they do on Carrie. Millie sighed, began talking about radio programs (their favorites are crime programs, which scare them half sick; they are in love with Sam Spade) and suddenly halted. "We've never given out that receipt."

She paused, and nothing seemed of greater importance than watching me light a cigarette. "Need an ash tray." She went to rinse out her saucer and bring it to me though not, being fearful of fires, without first filling it half full of water. The water was to extinguish the ashes immediately. She breathed more easily when, by habit, I rested my cigarette in the tray and it also went out. Then she went on. "You take some ducks—"

"Wait. I'll get all mixed up. Just take one duck."

Millie has a gimlet eye when necessary. "What's one duck good for?"

"Well, I don't know. Some people can't afford more than one duck at a time."

"Should get better jobs then," Millie answered.

"It might be," I said, "that you're cooking this duck for only two people. They only want to *eat* one duck."

Millie was musing to herself. "You'd think your friends could strike for better wages, just like anyone else does these days, if they don't get enough food to fill their stomachs."

I said, "All right, take some ducks."

"You'd do better to watch how you spend other people's pennies, especially people in a picket line," Millie said. "Take one duck—"

"You put that duck right down," Miss Carrie said, and was

on her feet. "We'll send something substantial along for his friends."

I didn't ask which friends, because I knew she would answer those pickets, but I did say that none of my friends were starving.

"Oughtn't be ashamed of friends because they're poor," Miss Carrie answered me from the pantry.

I started home with a basket of homemade bread, pickled pears and peaches, garlic dill pickles, canned tomatoes, and the rest of the banana pie. By mistake Millie packed the saucer I had been using as an ash tray, with water, and so the basket had to be unpacked, its contents dried off, and then packed again. Then she wiped the saucer dry and put it back in the basket. When I reminded her that she was making a mistake and that it was part of their good cup-and-saucer set, she smiled pleasantly, if baffledly, and put the cup in, too.

I felt strangely laden, driving away from their house—I had not expected such bounty. Something was being thrust on me, without my wanting it: a sense of community, perhaps. When I looked back, the startling thought struck me. I had neighbors.

I had never had any in New York, other than a succession of faceless building superintendents, the last of these having been my neighbor by virtue of the fifth of whisky I gave him each month, in exchange for which he surlily let me use his telephone during the war months when I could not get a phone of my own. In a city, neighbors weren't necessary, or even desirable. There were too many other things to fill one's time, besides stopping to chat with the people next door. Besides, big cities spawn a love of secrecy. You don't want everyone else to know what you're doing. Somehow, it isn't safe.

But now my new neighbors—inadvertently acquired, or had some intuition purposely propelled me up their road?—were both standing on their porch, waving good night. Then I saw them go inside, trying to squeeze through the doorway together.

Something had begun or ended. It was an unnerving sensation. The trick that had brought me to the country and then trapped me here—was there reason in it after all? I drove past the house I had finished building the autumn before, high and shadowy on a hilltop. The house, though new, seemed to have settled a little more comfortably into the land. I still felt angry, though, recalling how that house, begun with such joy, had become a trap. I thought of Joe, who had built the house, and how it had trapped him too. . . . Strange snares lurked among those sleeping hills.

I didn't want to go into the house tonight. It was lonely, living there alone, in the rooms that had been planned for laughing, easygoing crowds of friends. It was to have been only a summer house, with New York friends arriving to sun on its terraces, sit in its gardens, drink and talk at night in the big farm kitchen. But it had never had a party in it. The friends had never been invited.

I went instead down to the tavern at the Corners, a glum, slanting, ramshackle saloon called the Festive Country Club. A half-dozen farmers and their wives, who lived in the hills surrounding me, straggled along the unfestive bar. These farmers of the hills are of Welsh descent, and the Welsh—or Walshmen, they say—are a calm, reserved, stand-offish people. They do not believe in drinking and so in our village a half-mile away no taverns are permitted, but they all come down to the Corners to drink instead—as if, down there, they cease to be the same people who voted soberfacedly against alcohol at the last township meeting.

Often you can hear Welsh hymns coming from the Festive

Country Club. The Welsh sing their hymns with great thought-fulness, style, and dolorousness and they sound no less holy at a bar, interspersed with juke-box tunes. Nor does anyone sense an anachronism. Maybe because they don't believe in drinking, anyway.

No one spoke to me at the bar. It had been a tacit under-standing between us for more than a year. They looked at me politely, but walked in a discreet circle around me on their way to the pinball machine.

Finally Hank and his wife Mary, who own the slaughter-house, took stools next to mine.

"Saw you at the church supper last night." Mary is in her fifties and has the true Welsh glittery eyes that always belie their reserve. For a year she had seen me around and never spoken to me; but church suppers create bonds. I was shying away, when she added, "And I hear you've been up to the Lit-tens tonight."

It's the way you "hear things" in the country, almost before they've happened.

Mary was buying me a beer. It suddenly occurred to me that at the Festive no one ever drank by himself, but always in-cluded his neighbors. "Poor girls," she was going on. "They're dead tired. Lived with their brother up the road there until he died a few years ago. A real bastard. Had them out plowing and hoeing every day from dawn till dark, ever since they've been about ten years old. Those poor old girls deserve some fun."

"I think they're getting it now," I answered. "More than you know. They're cagey. I asked for their duck recipe and—"

"You didn't!" Mary said. She ignored my surprise. "You strangers move out here and don't know what's cooking. No one around here'd think of asking them that. That sauerkraut-duck is what they're famous for. It's the one thing they've got nobody's got."

I was still surprised. "Why get so upset about a recipe?"

Mary looked sad. "Outsiders," she murmured. "You damned outsiders."

I felt a chill wind blowing. But it was blowing from the opposite direction now. Outsiders. . . .

I got out of the bar. So let the wind blow, I thought, down those dark, twisting roads. But I'll keep riding along them alone.

2

Master Builder

W HY don't you run out to the Welsh Hills and take a look at the old Roberts Place?" my mother had suggested. "You remember—it's that rundown piece of land right next door to where Grandpa's farm used to be. Don't you remember, when you were a small boy, we'd take you out there sometimes for picnics?"

Dimly I remembered. My grandfather had died when I was a boy. But still, occasionally, the entire family, who lived not far away, in Milwaukee, would gather on breezy summer Sundays for a reunion in the woods and hills that had once been his. Out of my childhood, I could still recall those shadowy hills and woods, and tablecloths spread on the cool floor of the grove, and older men playing baseball, and the women busy with knives and forks and bowls of salad and baskets of sandwiches.

"And since you're got to leave New York for a while," my

mother went on, "and want to build yourself a house in the country—well, why not take a look at the old place? I heard from Cousin Erna the other day it's still for sale. No one's even lived on the land for twenty or thirty years—"

Her eyes held a soft, shrewd, gray-eyed wisdom. I had finally come home to Wisconsin to rest, after the long-delayed visit to a kindly, but nevertheless expensive, New York doctor. Too much work, plodding for success, more work, wanting quicker, bigger successes, causes havoc with the nerves, the heart, the pressure of the blood. . . . All this that I had known for months, he told me. Only now I was ready to listen. I had begun the embarrassing and unmanly habit of bursting into tears when anyone spoke to me—even the elevator girl when she asked what floor.

"Six months out of the city, some place quiet in the country, and you'll be yourself again," he promised. "And I'd advise you to get out of town for at least half of each year afterward. It's a good policy for people in your line of work. Say you're in advertising?"

I nodded.

"Madman," he said. "Well, go on. Get some fresh air."

It sounded, in part, like a reasonable idea. I was too frightened not to agree. I had always wanted a country place—and if these six months of idleness and absence were to be forced on me, why not let them be pleasant? Why not accept them in Wisconsin on familiar land among the Welsh Hills, where my grandparents and my parents had been reared, though they had all died or scattered now? Even the family name was already forgotten out there. It would be enjoyable, and somehow fitting, to hear it spoken once more across this rolling pocket of earth.

Too, I would enjoy having my mother nearby in Milwaukee, where she still lived; and she could know these hills again. Six months in the Welsh Hills, six months in New York. A new office account, acquired just before my nerves had blown apart, made the country house a possibility. Friends from New York would visit me there. I could hear them laughing, eating, drinking, making love, wandering through the meadows, over the hills. A country vacation would be restorative, and always New York would be waiting for me to return, placidly, perhaps, but even so with its peculiar challenge, as it had greeted me when I first arrived there.

Much of me, I thought, still loved New York now as I had then, ten years before, when I believed all men's triumphs shone at their brightest on that tiny, river-girt island. I had come there poor, anonymous, eager—what better way to besiege the queen American city? And the city, at first, seemed to answer me. Lights blinked; buildings soared (the braver was I to climb them); tugs hooted. I was going to become a writer. I hardly noticed the months passing in an impersonal hotel room, in which no story somehow got written, and more months as a flunky in a radio network office, with no time to write my own stories now, and then a few years of radio ghostwriting, during which the stories were forgotten altogether. And more years passing, and better and faster jobs . . . and never did I think I loved New York less, that the rivers flowed less enchantedly around this small, loud island.

Six months would end, and the time would come to go home again to New York, more work, quicker, bigger successes, new clients, new accounts. I felt better already. The terrible apprehensions in the middle of the night became less nagging, less terrible. I would even awake hearing strange music, like a siren's song, but the music was soothing now. I could hear no deception in it. The beginning of the big joke. . . .

*   *   *

I bought the forty acres of the Roberts Place on first sight. There was enough money for that, for a house, and the six months' combined holiday and rest while the house was being built. When those months ended, I'd be fit to return to the office and quickly replenish all I had spent. It was as easy as that.

I saw the greening oaks and lacelike wild grapes in bloom and the budding wild plums in the woods on a late afternoon in May. It was misty and cool. For the first time, I climbed the hills. There was expansion, silence, and emptiness—a feeling that no one had walked here for years. The last footfalls might have been my own, as a child, and my mother's and father's, when we picnicked last in the grove.

I strolled down to a lower ridge, looking southward down the long meadow, its grasses a silvery green in the fading light. This would be a nice place for a house, a summer house. Cows from a nearby farm were still pastured in the woods and they made a peaceable kingdom under the trees. I smelled all the land alive with bloom—even, in that instant, sensed danger, so that I hastily reassured myself I'd be leaving here again soon. *Six months, six months,* over and over I repeated it.

Then I saw a fox go streaking up the hillside. I had disturbed his land, his thickets and den, and he was escaping to his freedom. He did not welcome me. I was glad of that. After a little while, I'd happily let him have his home back again.

But this was the fox that Joe, who built the house, was

doomed to fall in love with. It was the fox that, in my turn, I too would follow, searching freedom along with him.

That May afternoon, however, he was no more than a streak of brown, seen briefly, then gone.

* * *

Joe was the rare, almost obsolete kind of builder who loved his work, and took enjoyment in every clank of his hammer and thrust of his saw. Unknown to himself, he was a master builder.He was a small man, still young, under fifty, rather wiry, quiet, but shyly amiable. And proud. He would not use a stick of lumber in the framework unless it was seasoned and sound—though there were shortages, he searched, waited, then searched some more until he found what he wanted. Every corner was mitered true. Doors and windows fit in their frames, joined in some forgotten carpenter's heaven. The foundation was solid and everlasting, and when the house was finished it had been built to last for centuries like the houses our forefathers built.

Joe lived in a near-by good-sized town. His father and grandfather had built many of the houses around the countryside—I had been especially impressed by the Trenchblow place his grandfather had built years ago, its outbuildings and barns, on a moonlit night, standing big, chunky and solid, like a herd of grazing steers. But Joe had moved away and become a city builder.

I arranged for him to meet me in the village grocery, so I could show him the land. He was waiting at the counter when I came in, and he despondently twitched a muscle when he saw me, raising his hand to push his cap back on his head. Then he lifted the cap slightly and settled it again. A cigarette salesman with a portable screen and sound equipment was showing a film of Frank Sinatra singing, inside the store. There was no one else in the store except Joe and Harry, who runs it, but the salesman ran off the reel and when it was ended, he began to deliver a loud, clear, memorized speech about his brand of cigarettes, with rehearsed gestures and facial expressions and thumping his fist in his palm, as if he had an audience of at least an enraptured hundred.

Joe leaned against the counter, listening politely so as not to hurt the salesman's feelings, rubbing an ear with one finger occasionally, his face rapt, though I could see his eyes tracing a box elder bug flashing its red jerky way across the floor. When the salesman had finished, he helped him pack up his projector and reels, and carry them out to the car. Then the salesman offered Joe a sample package of cigarettes, but Joe shook his head. He didn't smoke. But he had listened attentively, so as not to let the young salesman down.

Then he came back to me, and we shook hands. "Pretty speech, though," he said. "Nuts. I could never memorize a piece that long."

We decided to drive over in my car, Joe bouncing beside me taciturnly and narrowing his sharp gopher's eyes when we reached the low, glacial hills. In spring and summer, I know now, these hills are a wall of pleasant green silence. In winter they lie like a ring of gray and blue camels sleeping on the dunes of snow.

Joe got out of the car, looking about him critically. "What you want to leave New York for, and build a house out here in the sticks a thousand miles from nowhere?" He kicked the ground. "Not even good farm land. You won't be able to raise a crop worth a dime. The money you'll spend on this place, you could build a nice duplex in town. Have a good investment for the rest of your life."

I didn't answer that I was not here of my own choice. I only said that I didn't think I would try to earn a living farming. Anyway, it was only a house to live in half of each year. And in my heart, I was agreeing with him.

But then Joe looked toward the hills again, to the blowing, green arches of oak and the stabbing pink of shooting stars in the hollow. Suddenly his face cracked in a grin.

"Look, that goddamn fox, racing up the hill!"

He had seen it now, too—the fox I had seen on the first afternoon I looked at the hills. Again there was the curious sensation that it streaked off joyfully to freedom.

"Look at it," I heard myself answering.

Joe seemed a little appeased then, as if he had been given some kind of an answer, though certainly not by me.

I found a country lake hotel to live in while the house was

being built. After a few weeks, when I'd drop up to watch Joe's progress, I would find him chuckling as he sawed and supervised and pounded.

"Saw that goddamn fox today!"

"No kidding?" I may even have been surly in my answer. It was becoming *his* fox.

But Joe still disapproved of the house. He was still a city builder, who liked to erect apartment houses or duplexes or store buildings with modern bakelite fronts. As well as by the location, high on a hill, surrounded by woods, he was confounded by the design of the house. It did little good to answer him that, if I had to live in the country, at least I would live in the kind of house I wanted.

Joe shook his head. His wife ought to hear about this place.

Why did I need a kitchen the size of an old farmhouse kitchen, with a fireplace in it? Good-humoredly, but with an admixture of wonder, he kept asking what a wife (I didn't have one, I reminded him. "Ought to," he answered) would say to a kitchen where you had to walk a mile each day, traveling from the cupboards to the stove and back again. Why couldn't I have a small efficient kitchen like he put in all those neat duplexes he built?

A troubled look would come into his eyes that told of something peculiar happening to him, though he did not know what it was. It was something creeping into him insidiously. But he couldn't spot it.

He hadn't, I suppose, the faintest inkling of what was to happen to him. I even began to envy him, because it was happening to him and not to me. There was, I told myself, no reason for it to happen to me. This was a house of expedience, not of love. Even so, I often found myself arguing sharply with Joe.

He began to look more youthful, at the same time that he grew more sober and thoughtful. He'd ignore my arguments and knock off work to go look in the woods for the fox or his den. Or he'd reappear from the woods with a clumsy bunch of Queen Anne's lace in his hand, glancing at it scornfully as he tossed it into his truck. "Dragging it home for the Mrs.—she likes that kind of stuff," he'd say.

He seemed to expand, having more freedom about him. Or he'd linger after his workmen had left and walk around the half-built house tapping thoughtfully at the walls, not so much with a tap as with a lover's caress, or tinker with one of the sliding windows that filled one living-room wall looking down over the meadow, though they already slid in their grooves perfectly; or, alone and in the dark, test out one of the fireplaces and squat in silence before the fire, idly dropping in chips of bark or juniper boughs for the fragrance. What he thought then I don't know. What does any man think about in the silences of his love? His wife, he grinned, was complaining because he kept coming home later and later. He grinned considerably, with increasing shyness. For what he did not know was that he was falling in love.

With a house. Not my house, but the house *he* was building. As his father and grandfather had loved their houses, as my grandfather on the neighboring land had loved his. It was a continual surprise to him. An instinctive feeling for solidity and simplicity and texture returned to him, like something remembered from childhood. He was discovering a mastery in himself he had not even known he had, and perhaps did not even know he was discovering it—that was what befuddled him. As a result, he jeered maliciously at the floor plans, or wisecracked with soft scorn about the double doors in the bedroom. I didn't need more doors, least of all in a bedroom. Later I learned he already had the doors, stacked outside the house under a tarpaulin, waiting to be put in. He wanted to argue just to convince himself, half in delight, that what he was doing was right.

I argued back that I wanted the doors for no other reason than to be able to step from bed right into the woods.

"I'll be damned," Joe chuckled—but it made me glance at him in surprise, because there was plainly such pride in his voice.

*   *   *

He built the house exactly to plan and grew more silent as the job was nearly done, working from the first pale-green streak of morning till the full blow of September sunset behind the west hills. He beetled his brow while affixing the right, durable hardware and took one swift poke at the furnace man when he caught him using cheap second-hand tin for the flues. Then one day he caught Les Broderick, the painter, varnishing the floors. "Anything wrong with a clean naked grain?" he asked Les with quiet scorn, and Joe spent the night scraping the varnish off with remover, until the floor was bare as an unkissed cheek, and only waxing and rubbing and age would bring alive its rightful, mellow blush. He had remembered his father used to finish floors that way.

As the house neared completion, there was one last argument about the beams.

They were to support the overhang, facing the long meadow southward. They were beams from an old barn, hand-hewn, ancient, ten inches square, still solid, firm, but weathered to a soft silver-gray pigeon-like color.

"You can't wreck a house with old lumber like that," Joe said. "I can find some good new posts."

I shook my head. "I bought these from the farmer next door. They were in one of my grandfather's barns. He must have hewn them himself, sixty or seventy years ago."

"Well, use the old ones if you want," he said grudgingly, "but at least we'll plane 'em smooth and throw a good coat of paint on. Don't want wormy timber spoiling any house *of mine*."

Another shake.

"Hate to see rotten old beams like that standing up in front of *your house*," Joe said, but at the last two words looked at me strangely. He walked away.

Up went my grandfather's beams. The last hammer blow

rang melodiously from Joe's master hammer. I saw him walk a hundred paces down the meadow, turn, look back at the house he had built. The beams in the twilight must have shone soft as mist, silvery as feather. The house slept along the hilltop, a low rambling house of white clapboard with black roof, fat chimney. The many windows looked ready for motion, enjoyment, and life behind them in the rooms. Lamps would soon be lighted inside them. Soon my New York friends would arrive. . . .

There was a lazy, drifting, end-of-summer warmth that occasionally made rifts in the cool evening. The sky was turning the color of wild grapes.

Joe came back up to the house and tapped one of the beams. "Looks nice," he murmured.

*   *   *

The house was nearly finished. The six months, too, were more than ended. I was past due at the office. The summer in the country had done its work, as the doctor had promised: nerves calm, heart steady, pulse normal. Nights were for sleeping again, not for chasing shapeless and senseless fears. Joe busied himself with last details—latches on doors, planing down a window that stuck, taking longer over these small details than it seemed he ought. I wanted to move into the house, spend a week or two there, then lock up, leave, return to New York where everything was waiting. I was ready to grapple again.

It would have to be an earnest grapple. The house had cost twice as much as I had planned. Joe, in his thoroughness and craftsmanship, had argued for more solid woods, a year-round furnace to keep the house dry, a dozen other details I had not planned on. It had been necessary to borrow money from the village bank—loaned to me with surprising speed and cordiality. But that hardly mattered. I was more than eager to come to grips. . . .

Except the big joke. At the end of October, the wire came from the office. From Pollock, one of the first I planned on inviting out. SORRY COULDN'T HOLD POSITION OPEN ANY LONGER STOP AFTER MEETING TODAY HAVE TURNED ALL YOUR ACCOUNTS OVER TO STANLEY MERRIAM HOW'S YOUR HEALTH KEEP PLUGGING GOOD LUCK ERNIE.

I answered without too much alarm. THEN WHAT CLIENTS WILL YOU WANT ME TO HANDLE CAN RETURN IN ONE WEEK.

NONE.

WHY NOT?

REORGANIZED ENTIRE OFFICE STOP NO VACANCIES STOP HOPE YOUR HEALTH IS KEEPING STOP LOVE ERNIE.

THEN HOW IN BLAZES AM I SUPPOSED TO EARN A LIVING?

WHY DON'T YOU WRITE A BOOK LOVE ERNIE.

WOULD YOU COME OUT SEE ME AND TALK THINGS OVER STOP HAVE BUILT A LOVELY PLACE ANXIOUS TO HAVE YOU VISIT.

CAN'T SORRY LOVE ERNIE.

As the leaves fell, as the earth prepared for sleep, I began to understand that I might have to spend the winter in the Welsh Hills—which, all at once, looked cold. They seemed to close around me in impatience. I could escape them, of course.

I could go to New York, find other agencies, other clients and accounts. . . .

Only, there was no money left to live on while I beat my way around New York and got myself on my feet again. Nevertheless, I still could make it. Except that the loud, wracked nights had begun once more. The sound of night wind became thunderous—it blew all sleep away. I felt my nerves pull tight again, then snap, like rubber bands. My heart raced without provocation. In panic I watched all that the summer months had done become undone. Quickly I packed my bags. A day or two more and Joe would have the house finished, ready to lock up for the winter. I could abandon it, flee from it.

As an afterthought, or perhaps final precaution, I stopped in at the village doctor's office. Dr. Beemiller is a chunky, friendly man, but his eyes kept blinking nervously.

"I doubt if you could take a New York winter right now—your nerves and blood pressure. Hypertension. Not too good, man. Take it easy. And I don't like the way you've been loading yourself with sleeping pills. What kind of business you say you're in back there?"

"Advertising." I said it clearly.

"Pretty rough business? Hard work?"

I nodded.

He shook his head. "You'd never make it. I'll tell you, you spend six months or so right here in the country where it's quiet—"

"But I've just spent six months here, quiet as a mummy! And I've got to earn a living—"

Dr. Beemiller smiled. "Why?"

"*Why* earn a living?"

"Haven't you got a roof to sleep under, and a good-sized

piece of land? What's the matter, man? You just stay here."
He looked at me soberly. "You'd really better."

As I drove home, I noticed the last leaves had fallen from
the trees.

*   *   *

Joe was in the meadow when I got there. The house was finished but still he drove out each day, wandering about alone,
scowling, viewing the house from different hilltops, from the
meadow, shaking his head. Like the fox, it would make me
think. He had escaped to freedom; by rights, the house belonged to him. Everything good and solid about it, *he* had

made. He had used his inheritance, and built himself right into the house.

And this very house, suddenly, was one I hated. We both stood looking at it for a while. Then with a kind of wild pride, Joe came stamping toward me over the terrace.

He jerked his head. A brown blaze was shooting through the high dry grasses of the meadow, up toward the naked hills.

"There he goes—look at that goddamn fox," Joe shouted.

He was grinning. I felt a quick, angry uneasiness. Because the house had trapped me, and because at last I wanted to get rid of Joe.

"Well, it's all over, Joe," I said. "You did a wonderful job. Thanks. You're the Master Builder."

He was following me toward the door. "What's that you called me?"

"Master Builder. Name of a play."

I stepped inside, and a sudden clutch of wind took the doorknob from my hand and slammed the door shut. It is a solid door, without glass. A barrier, strong and impenetrable. I swung the door open again. I had seen Joe take a quick, desperate lurch forward as the door slammed shut.

But now he stood with a look of fright and horror on his face. There was even an instant's hate. He was locked out. But part of him was locked inside the house forever.

Nothing helped. "For Christ's sake, I'm sorry, Joe. I feel rotten. I've just had bad news. Come on in and have a drink with me."

He stood there for a minute looking blankly at me, and then shuffled off toward his truck. "Can't. The Mrs.'ll kill me. Late for supper now."

A new master was inside his house. One who did not love it. Often, during that first long painful winter, I would wake in the dead of night. My eyes would turn through the windows out to the snow-buried hills. Sometimes, it seemed, I would see Joe standing there, motionless, the master-builder staring down at his master-house in which he could not live.

3

The Willow Road and the Yokel

MOVE out here for any reason? Seems to me, if a man built a house like this, he'd enjoy living in it." Bud Devere, that second spring, persisted in being a friend.

"I came out because I was sick."

"Still sick?" Bud looked worried.

I was not certain how to answer. It was more than half a year since that day the leaves fell from the trees and Dr. Beemiller in the village had told me I could not return to New York. The solitude, the air, the lazy nights and lazier mornings, the view of the sleeping hills, the limitless sky, all had done their repairs a second time. But more had happened that winter. The body and nerves were healing again; not so, the spirit. I might have built this house nearer New York among the steep waterfalled hills of Connecticut, or on the green and sandy shores of New Jersey. But I had returned to Wisconsin because it was still my mother's home. I had liked to think of her visiting these familiar hills again. During the winter, she died. Now that reason, too, for ever loving this land was gone.

Bud was watching me speculatively. At last, he answered himself. "Doc Beemiller tells me you're in pretty good shape again. Built yourself up fine. So if you're better, why do you stick around?"

It was a question I had begun to ask myself. "I don't know. I just keep staying. It's tough to get started again in a place like New York. It takes dough—"

Bud nodded, like a wise man, agreeing. "Those magazine stories you've been writing," he said after a while. "They're not too bad."

I didn't know then it was a compliment, or I might have answered.

"Not bad at all," Bud went on. "Heard you might write a book."

"Might. Or might not. Or maybe I am. Or maybe I'm not. What in hell for?"

"No kidding?" Bud grinned. "I used to feel the same way. Funny thing, when I came back here in July '46, the heart went out of me. Did you ever see the end of beauty?"

They weren't words I had expected to hear in the country. But Bud went on unassumingly.

"It's awful—seeing something like that end. My company'd hit the Italian beach towns, and we rubbed 'em out just like that. All of a sudden there was nothing—just dead towns. So when I came back home, the whole place here looked just like one of the towns I'd helped destroy. I'd watch the sun go down behind the church and the Post Office and the shadows would come in just the way they did among all that dead gray rubble of the beach towns. It was awful. God-awful."

He scowled. I noticed he was sweating, as if he had recalled dead things that should have remained buried. It was an emotion I also was familiar with. He was watching me thoughtfully, with a slyness I had become used to seeing—that of a doctor watching his patient. He seemed to have made a decision, one that satisfied him. He was grinning again. But he spoke soberly.

"But people around here kept talking to me, and I worked my Dad's fields that summer, and after a few good benders down at the Corners with some girls that'd grown up while I was gone, and then a few drives after work along the Willow Road, I began to wake up again. When the locusts bloom over on Wallie Cwym's place, and you see Grandma Mills out in the noon sun hoeing her muskmelon hills—she's over eighty, you know?—and you spend a few days hunting in your woods —did you know you spoiled the best pheasant hunting in the county by building your place up here and scaring 'em off?— and you start eating some of Hank's fresh sausages right out of the slaughterhouse, and breathing air, and sleeping nights, you can't stay sore at anything long." He lit my cigarette from the butt of his and grinned again. "By the way, how's the show at the Copa these days?"

Most people who have never lived in the country have a peculiar idea of what farmers are like—static, naturally bucolic, and circumscribed by their own fences. It was my own assumption, too. Bud Devere fixed that. He knew the last corners of the earth, and not only because the Army took him there but because when he was there he took the time to absorb what he saw—a trick he seemed to have appointed himself to teach me. Even at home again, he didn't have to go far to enjoy the full prickly excitement of travel.

He was in his late twenties, burly, which made his omnipresent consideration even more surprising, and he liked to talk. He came up for evening sessions of talk—uninvited, mostly, which did not bother him, and often unwelcome, which also did not seem to trouble him. Gazing out over the long meadow, he would ramble on inexhaustibly, peppering his talk with sly barbs about people who couldn't be satisfied where they were, people who thought the grass was greener on the other side of the fence—people, more precisely, who thought life was lived only in New York. Sometimes he'd wander off into politics and the A-bomb or the Genesee ball team or music or fishing. But he'd always end up in New York. He liked New York. But he also liked being where he was.

Imperceptibly he would slip into talk about yokels. At such times we would eye each other, not sympathetically. It was confusing, and never quite clear which he thought were the yokels —New Yorkers or his own people. Himself or me.

He would break into laughter. It was amiable, but a little mocking. "You ever been up the Statue of Liberty?"

"Well, that's more the thing for tourists to do in New York." It was my point. Tourists meant him.

"For Christ's sake, what you live there for? Ever take the boat trip around Manhattan Island?"

"That's one thing I always meant to do. I hear it's—"

"You *hear!*" Bud said, and clapped my shoulder. "But you never went. One of the prettiest cruises I ever went on."

"New Yorkers don't have time for that kind of sightseeing. It's more for tourists—" I repeated the word carefully.

"Didn't know there was anything else but in New York," Bud answered. His voice had grown softer. "Everyone comes from somewhere. It's a pretty town, though."

I began to wonder if I had ever enjoyed New York, or loved it so much as I thought. I thought uncomfortably of what my own travels there had really been like—from Central Park down to Times Square by way of the Oak Room, 21, the Blue Angel, the Broadway theaters, the RKO building, and the Museum of

Modern Art. A few times I had strayed as far afield as the Bronx, to see the okapi at the Zoo; or Wall Street, when a visiting lady cousin insisted on seeing Trinity Church. But there had never been time for more.

"Ever go up the Willow Road?" Bud asked suddenly.

"Where's that?" My mind was still on Manhattan Island. "Is that the one off the Bronx Parkway—?"

Bud laughed. "It's a mile from here. I'll take you over it someday."

*   *   *

A week later he drove up in late afternoon. He said he thought I'd like to see the Willow Road. I said I thought I didn't—I still preferred driving over those roads alone.

Bud looked me over thoughtfully. Prickles of sweat came on his broad, sunburnt forehead. He was still wearing his field clothes and smelled of fields and work and farm animals, and looked as healthy as one. Again he seemed to be considering whether what he was doing was worth while. Then he flashed his needling grin at me. His burly hands took a firm grip on his steering wheel.

"Get in, yokel, and I'll show you some sights."

I thought I heard, behind his words, the countryman's vague dislike of strangers—it is apt to pop up anytime when least expected, like spontaneous combustion in a farmer's barn. But if it was there, it soon disappeared.

So did, gradually, my assurance that farmers are no more than heavy-footed rustics. Bud—I would not admit it then—will always be foot loose, though he may never leave our county again. He has the globetrotter's vision, even if he is traveling no farther than to our general store for a pack of cigarettes. An uncomfortable thought began to glimmer again in the back of my mind ... circumscribed by high buildings, was I the one who had never been anywhere?

I did not want to see what Bud saw. But the reluctance began fading away in me, that first time we went down the Willow Road. It covers scarcely more than a mile, but in that mile you can travel a thousand miles. Bud nudged me and murmured, "Here she begins," when we reached the nearby crossroads named Beddoesville, one of the loveliest and most remote-looking crossroads I have seen anywhere, with its towering and black and ponderous elms, and beneath them a handful of one-hundred-year-old (which is Methuselan in the Midwest) small white clapboard houses as charming and architecturally satisfying as any in New England. How these four or five houses got here, nobody knows. They look as if part of New Hampshire or Vermont had blown away, and settled down among our more usual and neat but not impressive farmhouses.

Bud kept silent. He wanted me to open my own eyes. He even pretended indifference, whistling to himself, but I knew how earnestly he hoped I was seeing what he had brought me to see. Since then, I've learned how many country people know and revere this art of enjoying the small scene and event, the birth of a calf, a remembered spot, the tumultuous labor and excitement of feeding the threshers, who come like locusts and swarm over your farm for a day and disappear again at night, the annual Welsh singing competition in the village—these are the great and proper events of a lifetime.

Bud turned left at the crossroads and stopped his car. On one side stood Mountain Ash Farm—not a farm really, despite the big carved sign that said so, but more like the country abode of some 1910 romance-heroine, with its huge square white house and pergolas and thick natural woods before it, blowing with shadows of grape hyacinth and narcissus that spring.

There is a small lake in which, as often as I've driven by since, I have never seen anyone swim, and plantings of wildflowers that tend themselves, and behind the house a tremendous cutting garden in which I have never seen anyone working or cutting a flower.

I have never seen anyone moving in or around the house, though my neighbors say an old woman still lives there, and whenever I see Mountain Ash Farm a word jumps into my head. Pre-war. "Pre-" any war, somehow, for there is a feeling of well-earned opulence and stability and a strong pull of peace on this strange corner of a busy highway, and I imagine there is always a well-filled bread bin in that house, good talk, and sound sleep at night after a day of work. I think I know why Bud wanted me to see that house, firm as I was in my refusal to love the country. It looks indestructible, like an act of decency or hope. It is both a reminder and a memory, impervious to bombs or any other kind of destruction such as ruined cities. I suspect too, the hidden old lady will live on forever, though she might be forgotten.

But on the other side of the road, like a warning, was an old stone building, built of the same pale pinkish stone the Welsh settlers were to use later in building their homes throughout these hills. It once must have been either a stable for the big place or else housed a blacksmith's shop.

Bud broke his silence. "Funny thing, not a single living soul around here can remember when this building wasn't empty. But it must have been a blacksmith's shop sometime—once I found a half-dozen rusty horseshoe nails in the weeds over there against the wall. But not a soul around here even remembers a story about the old place. Funny to think of that nonexistent blacksmith pounding away in his shop there a long time ago—so long ago there isn't even a grave around here for him. How can the past just disappear like that, as if it never happened?" How could it? For all I know, Bud might have been remembering the beach towns. For the only time I saw him look self-conscious. "You know what I'd like to see here? I'd like to see some real oldtime honest craftsman living here" —like Joe, I thought—"maybe a cabinetmaker, polishing away at his rare old woods. Or maybe one of those old stonecutters.

You know, the kind who chipped out all those monuments in old cemeteries?"

The colossal trumpeting angels, the heartbreakingly clasped hands, the crouching lambs. . . .

Bud raced the car along a few hundred feet. Then stopped, jumped out, leaped down a bank to a creek and came back with a dripping handful of watercress, like a merman dragging wet

seaweed. "Ma'll fix us this with bacon and vinegar and brown sugar, if you want to come around for supper—O.K.?" He shoved a fistful in my mouth. It was cold and damp and spicy and tasted fresh as spring itself.

The creek was edged by low hills, studded with junipers, tall, robust, standing silent and lonely as Indians up the hillsides. Bud got back into the car, fell silent again, swung the car right, and began the last brief stretch of winding road that encompasses such vast distances, if only you look to see them, for at each turn you seem to be in another part of the world.

There was an apple orchard to begin with, hidden by a low hill, so that only the foam of its blossoms could be seen, and one could imagine, in autumn sunlight, its lush haul of fruit, a whole skyful of apples. Bud cruised slowly around another turn and suddenly I was in France.

"When I was in Paris—" I began.

"Oh, you been there?" Bud asked kindly.

I fell silent.

This is where the willows are. There is a farmhouse and a narrow valley, and here the creek widens into a pond, and fringing the pond are the disconsolate, shimmering willows. The road is so rarely traveled (we met no traffic; I never have since) that the pond and trees might again be some forgotten, magic place. And across the pond is a straight row of high poplars, such as always line the country roads of France. I am always disappointed not to find grapes growing on the slope, and a peasant in wooden shoes and blue blouse drinking warm wine lazily under the poplars, and gulping thick sweetish plums, and downing thick slices of ham between long crusty hunks of French bread spread lavishly with sweet unsalted butter, as I once did under a row of poplars near a bridge at Joinville outside Paris, which in memory seems the best meal I have ever eaten. I thought of telling Bud this, but thought better of it. He knows France better than I do.

He laughed suddenly. "I was damned sure it'd remind you of France. There were so damned many rows of poplars just like this one in Normandy, along the road all the way up, and later when we came back every damned one of 'em was shot off. A land of stumps. If you ever get to France— Oh! You been there."

He had kept on driving, and France, its poplars, were gone. We were far in the awesome stillness of the northernmost tip of some vague Canadian province. Even the light changed, and fell in chilly slabs. For here was a desolate lake, and sometimes on later drives I have seen a solitary fishing boat on the lake, though no houses or other signs of habitation are visible around this turn.

There is a swamp, and the swamp abounds in tamaracks, some dead, like a cemetery of themselves, some feathery green, cone-studded, yet always gaunt-looking. There is a momentous feeling of discovery in that short curving stretch of road, of primevalness—I felt I was the first human being since the world began to lay eyes on that swamp, those trees. A moose coming there to drink would not have startled me.

I was glad that Bud stopped the car and decided to swim in the lake. When he shut off the motor the deathliness grew even greater, and a nearly-ended fear returned. I began sweating. Bud looked at me, seeming to worry. It was as if the trip down the Willow Road had helped not at all. There was the panic, the trapped feeling, the slow rising anger, just as it had always been there during the past long winter. . . .

"Come on!" Bud yelled harshly—he sounded annoyed, and afraid too. "For Christ's sake, get into the water!"

And once we were splashing in the water the frightening

lapse of life filled in—you could feel the heart start to beat again. The cold water, too, made the nerves stop throbbing. Afterwards we stretched out on the lake's gravelly edge.

I began remembering how, as a kid, on some lake near my grandfather's farm, this same forgotten lake perhaps, the sun had felt this same way on my body. Healing and revivifying. Bud was stretched out flat on his back, his arms flung apart. I knew he was thinking the same thing, feeling the same way. I began recalling all the times I had walked through New York, going no place. Behind my shut eyelids I could see the greenish images of all I had just seen on the Willow Road. I kept thinking how often I had had doubts and worried because I could not get back to New York (though I still would! I shouted to myself) and how I had resented being buried here among the yokels. I still was not reassured; the sun could not burn through all my resentment. I would still get away, back to a life of excitement, of sudden successes. . . .

Bud had reached over to tap me on the shoulder. "You're all right. Nice to have you in the neighborhood."

"Thanks." After a while, I added, "I keep wondering which one of us is the yokel?"

"Skip it," Bud said, with a relieved, magnanimous grin.

*   *   *

I learned later, too, much more about the Willow Road. Its troubling presence was like a strong scent, a pull toward some place other than those you've found on maps. After our swim, when we went back along it, it grew clearer. It took many more trips, with Bud or alone, or with friends or neighbors, before I could recognize fully what it was.

The road itself had a quality; it was narrow, rutted, crooked, and seemed endlessly to be leading somewhere—home, perhaps. This is what at last I came fully to know. You felt you had come a long way in search of this road. You imagined yourself walking along it as a child, a little fearful as night starts coming around you, touching the whispering leaves softly, so softly that you should not be afraid, but the silence on this road is so vast and palpable that it makes you want to run. You did not run, though, when you were this child, because like a package growing lighter under your arm at each step, you knew up ahead was all you ever wanted or needed—home, safety, comfort, someone who loved you more than anything else in the world.

All your life you keep looking for this road again.

4

The Very Tired Veery

I T WAS the road I had, perhaps, always been looking for, when I drove alone through the dark, chasing night.

The Willow Road made all other roads more enjoyable to travel. I learned how light and wind can change the landscape. Shadows made distant hills seem Alpine. Blowing flashes of light, as a cloud lifted, could turn a November pond into a glacier. Now that I was beginning to let myself have neighbors, their houses took on charms I had not noticed in them before— the slant of a roof, the mossy sturdiness of its shakes, the cool intricacies of an iron fence, the bursting beauty of a full barn.

Slowly, too, neighbors turned into friends, and I learned the pleasure of give and take. With none so keenly as with Millie and Carrie Litten. In our county there are many veeries. The song of this tawny-brown thrush is said to sound like *phfew!* More than once, driving along the roads I was growing to love, I would find myself moving in a certain, inevitable direction. Of its own accord, the car would come to a stop. And there I would hear the veeries singing—faintly, however, their *phfew!*

phfews! sounding weak with indescribable exhaustion—around the Littens' house.

Returning home from late drives, I would see their lights still burning, which was not unusual because they slept late in the morning, saying they've earned late rest, which they have. One night I passed by as late as three A.M. The house was in a glory of light, as for a party. But only deep silence and emptiness and the occasional call of a veery dipping around the house and yard accompanied the blaze, instead of a noisy crowd. I passed by, drove home, started to bed, only to find myself getting up again, lighting cigarettes, sitting before the living-room windows and watching for dawn to start rolling the uneasy darkness off the long meadow, a dawn which that morning would not come.

I argued with myself. Millie and Carrie are, after all, two maiden ladies in their sixties, kind, gently intuitive, and three A.M. in farming country is the hour for catarrh, rheumatism, the cunning vagaries of the blood's pressure, and even worse things, failure of the heart, rape, and death by fire or bludgeon. I thought I had better check anyway, taking a chance on the pandemonium of letting phones start ringing across our countryside, and called their number after I managed to wake up our sleepy but friendly operator—only to hear Miss Millie pick up the receiver, say nothing but "Shhh!" and hang up again.

That sent me back into my clothes, my car, and over the roads in a hurry. Knowing the Littens, I knew it might only mean they had listened to one of their favorite radio programs, like "Dragnet," that evening and were afraid to go to bed, which had happened before. Or they were watching for flying saucers, which also had happened. But I had to make sure. And a good thing I did, for I found Miss Carrie stretched out pale and trembling under a half-dozen shawls on the parlor couch, and

Miss Millie rocking beside her, solemn as the angel of death.
I knew why dawn would not come that night.

"Carrie's appendix just burst," Millie announced in a trum-
pet-like voice as I came in.

"Well, did you call Dr. Beemiller?" I asked. "You don't fool
with a case like that. When did you call him?" I glanced at my
watch. "When's he getting here?"

But in answer to my questions Millie only looked at me absently and in pitiful patience.

"How do you know it's burst?" I asked.

"Carrie says she heard it," Millie said.

"Well, if you called the doctor he'll be—" But I stopped.
From Millie's faint smile I understood she had not even called
for help. And I realized what a lost world it would be for either
of them, one without the other, and how this had frozen Millie
to helplessness. I rushed for the phone book, which they never
keep anywhere near their phone but in their bookcase along

with the dictionary, encyclopedia and mail-order catalogues—
logically, since it's a "book you look things up in"—and began
thumbing through for Dr. Beemiller's number.

"No use," Millie said, glancing at me sorrowfully. "Too late.
It's burst. Carrie heard it plain as day."

"But you can't just sit here and let Carrie die—"

"Lord's will," Carrie muttered from the couch, her eyes
closed. She looked all ready to be carried off.

"Nonsense. Mine burst a few years ago and they saved me,"
I said.

But both only sighed and shook their heads. It sent me into
a flurry at the telephone, waking up the operator again, then
waiting for her to wake up the doctor—he slept the sleep of ten
night operators. All the books I had read about country doctors
and their endless vigils soured in my brain.

But luckily, he slept on. After a while I think even the operator dozed off again, for I heard her stop ringing—the sound
grew fainter, like the veery's song, and then just died. Millie
and Carrie looked asleep too. In this land of dormice I was
growing frantic, shouting remembered instructions about an
ice pack, when Millie rose from her rocker in a burst of discovery.

"Carrie, I just remembered. Four years ago last spring, that
same year Aunt Dell had her twins? That same spring you *had*
your appendix out."

"So I did," Carrie said, getting up. She began folding the
shawls and putting them back in their cedar chest. She gave
me the look she sometimes does, as if I were a mild lunatic that
needed humoring, but could also be irksome, and I moved
quickly away from the phone.

"Remember exactly," Millie was going on, "how I brought
you the first Pasque flowers from Cow Hill to the hospital.

Brought along a bunch for Aunt Dell and the twins, too." She was poking the curtains at the window, looking out at the bright summer dawn that I had been sure would not come. "Looks like a pretty day. Come back after you've had your little nap," she said, turning to me with a sudden cheerfulness. "Nice day to go driving. Shouldn't waste a fair day."

"Pasque flowers or was it hepaticas?" Carrie asked, deep in thought at the cedar chest. "Seems like I brought those to you, Millie. Seems like it was *your* appendix we had out?"

Millie let the curtain drop into place. Both sisters were again growing pale. Carrie was reaching into the cedar chest to take out the shawls she had just put away. It was, as Millie had said, a beautiful morning with a watery freshness flowing down the hills—it seemed a shame to flout such a day and I left as politely as I could. Both, or either, whichever it was, must have recovered, though. When I finished my little nap at two that afternoon, I found a big coffee ring on the doorstep, along with a jar of fresh cream, slightly soured by now from the heat.

There was also a note, marked Personal. *We shouldn't have let you go home without breakfast. C.L., M.L.,* it said. They also enclosed their cards, the elaborate hand-written kind with the capital letters all swirling off to look like antlered reindeer.

5

To Right and Left

AUNT Dell is not really my aunt but everyone calls her Aunt Dell. She lives near our village and I've never heard her called anything else, not even by her husband or her own children. She is everybody's Aunt Dell. And in time I knew I was lucky and glad.

One thing that had been waiting in the country for me to find, if only I would, was time. In New York, you devoured time. Here, it wooed you. It had hung there, like ripe fruit asking to be picked, all during my first gloomy winter and spring. There was time to spend with neighbors. The spores of friendship had lain dormant a long while. Country people are cautious in what they offer outsiders because, once a friendship is mutually agreed upon, they offer so much. So a season of waiting hung in the air. But now slowly, imperceptibly, as seasons merge, the time of waiting ended.

Once the unspoken pact was made, once I had made the overture, even if reluctantly, that second spring at the church supper, neighbors appeared. Like morels in the woods, overnight from nowhere. Or rather, from everywhere. Millie and Carrie. Aunt Dell. The Waldeens, Ed and Paulie. The Fifes and Bud Devere and the Cwyns and Emlyn Jarvis, who spoke only Welsh, with a cleft palate at that.

Aunt Dell is tall, joyous, and white-haired, though the white has a mottled cast to it, both dismal and sunny, and though she shampoos it forever, she says, it never looks clean. Her children—there are always more than you remember—range from a tall, dark, Indian-looking daughter of thirty down to the young ash-blond twins. I soon learned that for all her bluster, she is an unbelievably kind woman, sheltering stray animals and tramps alike, bursting into tears at every movie she sees, even comic ones, and always organizing and taking over and gooddeeding, like the Christmas she prepared a half-dozen baskets for the poor, but then in our whole county could not find anyone poor enough to need a basket, though they bulged with geese and preserves and home-baked fruit cakes and puddings. But also she has another passion.

It is for breaking the heart—her own. She is doomed to expend her greatest love on the transient. A wanderer in town. A child visiting neighbors in summer. A temporary roomer, for whom she can always find room in spite of her family's sprawling size. Someone else's pet bird. A sick neighbor who stubbornly gets well and no longer needs her help or her soup. Movie actors, flickering momently on the screen. Heroines in books, vanishing at the turn of a page. Some unknown body, old or young, if she happens to pass a country church where a funeral is in progress—she will join the mourners and mourn as compassionately, and honestly, as any of them. After a brief stay each of these vanishes and Aunt Dell is left alone to grieve over her abundant lost friendship, only in a few days to pour her affection and devotion on someone or something else. Her love is a big empty basket never filled. Even in her garden love lies wasted, for in her mysterious way she plants only what won't survive. No hardy pinks or stout myrtle, no common sturdy iris or ineradicable peonies or bleeding hearts (except her own) are planted there, none of that perennial group that will endure and multiply on neglect. But only the evanescent flower. The bloom condemned to die in the bud. Chrysanthemums that blossom too late, so that all she ever has of them for her bouquets are stalks of frostbitten buds. Vegetables, which are pure necessity, grow for her in profusion. But the flowers she loves, the trimmings of life, never. Her roses winterkill. Moles feast on her lily bulbs. Her delicate annuals shrivel under the first burst of summer sun. Unthinkingly, she calls forget-me-nots forget-me bushes—to Aunt Dell it must have the ring of truth.

A few times that second spring when I went to her house to buy eggs or poultry she greeted me pleasantly, but with reserve, and after that for a few more times we would wave to each other when we passed in our cars. Then suddenly, and as wantonly as spring comes, there at my door was Aunt Dell. She was driving an old enormous black Packard—she has a new huge used car every few months, all of which disintegrate under her lusty touch the moment she places herself behind the wheel. She has a passion for hugeness and old things. Her house is huge and old and always spotlessly clean; its furniture is comfortably ancient. When she rapped for the first time at my door, she managed to stand there hugely grinning.

"So, mister, isn't it maybe time we got acquainted?" she demanded, all good bright warmth.

"Oh. You're Aunt Dell. I know you already." But I was still wary.

"I'm Aunt Dell, he says. I guess I don't have another name, ainna?"

"What is the other name?"

She made a face. "Adelaide."

"I should have called you Mrs. Dell. But everyone around here—"

"Mrs. Dell? Who's that? Who's got such a name?" In case I wasn't being attentive, she jabbed a thick, amiable thumb into my chest. Then she stooped from her mighty height to look under a chair. "I don't see no Mrs. Dell around. No kidding, ainna?" The *ainna* always has a hiccupy emphasis. "But Aunt Dell, that's a somebody I know. Why, it's me!" And she went into a typhoon of laughter. When she subsided, you could still feel friendliness curling and uncurling like a small animal inside her commodious breast.

She was collecting donations for her Ladies' Aid remnant sale—all residents, male, female, of any creed, are expected to donate to these recurrent white-elephant sales. In time I discovered it to be a pleasant example of functioning brotherhood, because Catholics will donate old beds and discarded sewing machines to Welsh Presbyterians and the Presbyterians send over old lawn mowers and lopsided floor lamps to the Catholic sales.

For Aunt Dell, collecting donations (for anything) was a crusade. "Anything you got," she said, glancing happily about the room. "No matter what you thrun out, someone else can use it, see? And pay good money. All goes for charity, don't it? For our poor," she explained in sudden sadness, unmindful of her experience with the Christmas baskets and that there are no poor in our county. She smiled at me in pity, as if I were the neediest among them.

"Heard you ain't been feeling too well. Poor man. Heard it from Bud Devere—"

I began to explain overdeterminedly that I was all well again, fit as a fiddle, strong as an ox—the words were flowing in icy calm through my brain, but Aunt Dell's attention had wandered. She had spied the bamboo furniture in the living room. It was expensive, graceful furniture. I had bought it in anticipation of all my New York friends who would lounge against its cushions.

"Look," she cried. "All fishpoles!"

"Bamboo—"

"What I said, ainna? Fishpoles." She went to test it gingerly. "Holds me up?"

"Strong as iron," I said.

"Some fishpoles ain't," she said reflectively. But then she settled down, as if we were lifelong friends—in my living room which, up to now, had received few callers.

She began to tell me of her woes. They were great and lengthy. Her German parentage trumpeted itself each time she opened her mouth, emitting English words in German syntax, a kind of personal language in three-quarter time.

"It's that one kiddo of mine," she announced with a cheerful fury. I don't know why it should have, but it shocked me to see her haul out cigarettes and begin to puff on one, not heartily, but delicately. "My kiddo Buss. Gets me all the time in dutch, don't he? Since he's fourteen now, he should know better, ainna? Gets me so sore I could straggle him." And a gleeful pleasure was in her blue eyes at thought of "straggling" him, too.

Before long, I was beginning to wish I could find joy and beauty as Aunt Dell finds them. That day, and for no reason, she interrupted herself and asked to see the kitchen. I still was begrudging having neighbors trot through the house as they pleased—though by now Bud Devere had already made it his second home—but Aunt Dell, having no such un-neighborly impulses as I, rose from the fishpole sofa, and sailed her great bulk toward the kitchen door.

Once in the kitchen, she saw the coffee pot, and pounced on it as a mother might, rescuing her only child from contamination. She looked it over woefully. The pot was in all truth messy, since the coffee had boiled over that morning and the grounds had not yet been washed from its sides, prompting Aunt Dell to dash it under the faucet for a quick scouring like a human head on which she had just found lice.

"Look that poor percolator!" Tears really blistered her eyes —the poor percolator, indeed human, was shamefully mistreated. When it was bright and gleaming again, purified by her temporary searing compassion, she filled it with coffee and put it on the stove to boil. "Where's cups and saucers, mister?"

When cups and saucers and sugar and cream were waiting on the table, she seemed appeased. Accomplishment had triumphed. She put her tall body in a chair before the kitchen fireplace and looked for a moment sorrowfully down at the logs being consumed by fire. But apparently they did not merit full compassion. Or else she remembered how the percolator had been rescued, for a luxuriant ease slid over her, like an afghan. She gave a sigh that brimmed with joy, and was free to go on with her story.

"My kiddo Buss." Her words were high with alarm, though not without enjoyment of the catastrophe she was about to report. "First he drops me the temperature and then he picks me my maybells yet—!"

I memorized her words, as one might try to memorize a fragment of tormentingly beautiful music to hold in the inner ear. Later I deciphered them (after she had left with a not-too-generously-given donation for the sale) and understood that her kiddo Buss had broken her thermometer and then, without apparent reason, picked all the lilies-of-the-valley, one of the few flowers that will actually bloom there, from her garden. Buss apparently was a meddlesome, vandalic kiddo who certainly deserved to be straggled. It gave me odd comfort.

The donation she had wheedled out of me against my wishes, and carried away with her like a trophy of war, was a peculiar one. As she left the house, she spied an outdoor settee, the long kind you can lie on. It, too, had been bought in anticipation of the many cheerful, visiting friends who would sprawl in its turquoise languor. But since I had been trapped in the house alone all winter, I had not even bothered to move it inside. It was part of the house I had ceased to love.

The long winter, the snows, the thaws, the downpours of early spring, all had ravaged it. It was faded and pale. To Aunt Dell, however, it looked inviting. She dropped into it, experimenting, stretching supine, feet poking up, her strong arms locked behind her head. She looked wonderfully prosperous and relaxed. "Look, I'm at the Ritz now, ainna?"

Buss, as yet unstraggled, and another older son came up later with the truck to cart it away. But I don't think it got to the sale. One day that summer I went past her house and there it was on her front lawn, and there she was, stretched out luxuriously at the Ritz, big as life—which is exactly how big and vital she is. She doesn't know it, but she's always been at the Ritz. And I didn't know it then but know it now—her lucky kind always is.

*   *   *

If Aunt Dell bloomed with sunny vigor on one side, then in another house nearby the Waldeens lived in a silence as autumnal and secret as mine had been.

But theirs had another reason. And they had not always been secretive. Their withdrawal began mysteriously in the same year that mine had ended. For a while, after I first became friends with them, they were, like Bud Devere, the cool, restful figures in a shady landscape.

Perhaps, I thought, as I grew to know them, it is too late for pioneers; but there was a new kind, revitalizing the old places, throwing a new kind of seed into the broken, sighing soil their grandfathers had cleared, as my grandfather once cleared soil on my neighboring acres. Growing to love neighbors like Ed and Paulie taught me this. That there was a gentry sprung from the earth, not alone from city mansions. They have an inner power in their eyes that demolishes cities. Where it came from I could not discover, unless from the registry or heraldry of their own spirits.

The Waldeens were in their early forties. Ed was a tall, gaunt farmer. Paula—though no one ever called her that but always Paulie, which fitted her size better—stood no higher than Ed's bottom rib. Ed had dark, sharp features that made him good-looking even by movie standards. Sometimes, at parties, he'd pick Paulie up and carry her under his long arm. As small as Paulie was, she was also that fragile. They could not have been more mismatched, in all things except their souls, where they met and completed each other. If they saw themselves in each other, as lovers do, then Paulie saw her strength in Ed, and Ed saw his gentleness and civility in her.

Ed made money because he bred and fed his cattle intelligently. Paulie's house was newly done over, with a picture window through which the view yanked the eye by leaps and bounds up to the rolling hills. At night curtains were drawn across the window (shocking behavior in the country, because what are you doing that you have to hide behind curtains?) and there in the attractive curtained room they read or talked and drank and entertained, which last was, almost always, in a casual dropping-in way.

They traveled a good deal, by plane if possible, wearing expensive clothes, at home in the best big hotels. But they always remained *country* gentry; they never wanted to be or considered themselves anything else. They returned from traveling and, at home, kept right on with their gay, gregarious, talkative life. Not in the nearby duked-up Welsh Hills Country Club, which their finances and style would have permitted, but at our village Firemen's Picnic or at Jerusalem Church suppers. They never thought they belonged elsewhere. They had no children. But Paulie often tended the neighbors', who were sometimes taller than she, while the neighbors fished or went into market or to the hospital to have another baby. Ed and Paulie drove a Buick convertible, with two extra cushions so Paulie could see from behind the wheel. At home, Ed lounged in old Navy work pants and Paulie wore ordinary shapeless housedresses— which, on her, you never noticed anyway.

Because what you saw was her face, the size of a doll's, framed in the ever-present babushka, a silk one for parties, cotton for working in the garden or fields. The babushka gave her face the effect of a piece of golden fruit, wrapped in tissue paper for special care. But even laughing, it was a face of shadow. Life pulled at her tiny muscles, it would not let her rest, and experience reflected upon and assimilated (and no complaints, either) shone in the small eye and forehead wrinkles—quality's face. It did not bother her that she was so small. But she did not play it for cuteness, either. There was nothing that dissembling in Paulie.

Her skin was smooth and thin but also looked tough as tree bark, pulled tight to a kind of luminosity over her face bones. Yet it always remained flexible, to madness nearly, for every flutter of emotion rode over it like a dinghy on a rough sea. Her mouth was as delineated as though it could show no deviation; but again as flexible, for that mouth became a hundred different mouths a day, when she laughed or scowled or spoke in high outrage (her voice had the pitch and timbre of a toy flute) against some farmer ruining his fields or his wife ruining her teeth. Her warm mouth became a hundred different kinds of bird, butterfly, moth, or other winged thing as her rapid words spelled out their transformation over it.

But her eyes were the repository of all that made Paulie Waldeen. Her love for big Ed, the fields, the village, neighbors, their barns and cattle, the done-over house, the sky, the kettles and bald domes of the hills, the weeds and seeds—all were plain in the eyes. They were small, but they looked larger and brighter than ordinary eyes. But in them also were the fierce power, the lessons, whatever they were, that made her able to love—in a way, enragedly determined to love. There were dark wings of something under her eyes. These same wings often rushed through her words, leaving a troubled echo of their passage when her high, plinking voice fell silent. You had the feeling that a pane of glass had been miraculously, beautifully shattered every time she spoke.

You swore to yourself, when you saw her vulnerable face, like that of a doll that forgot to stay a doll and grew up by mistake, that you would lay down your life to help her. But she never once needed your help—or anyone else's, except possibly Ed's.

The babushka-framed face laughed at you, like a strong, wise peasant's. She knew music, perched up terribly high on the piano stool before her grand piano, the small hands playing like big ones, and she read shrewdly, her forehead knotted into a thousand dwarf crow's-feet over the tall pages, and she talked strict, exciting common sense, and loved the land and the seasons and any weather. August that summer was one of fogs. Rather than bright-streaked cherry sunsets there were dusks of fog, with the fog like an old string bag catching half the countryside in its mesh. The blurred wet dusks were followed by deep evening seas of fog. It was miserable for everyone but Paulie. She and Ed went trudging through it to let its ghostly fingers rub on their cheeks, loving fog, the fog loving them, and her sighing laugh would continue, not for any reason other than a general approval of all the world.

They drank beer down at the Corners, joked with the mail carrier and the barber, served on the township schoolboard, entertained often, made up fishing parties, tried to start up a musical club, though no one would agree to perform except Paulie (with tall, big Ed standing proudly in the hall doorway, a smile on his lips while he watched her fingers racing like frantic children down the keyboard), dropped in often on friends and begged them to drop in on them. It was clearly a life of positive pleasure, all affirmation, gusto, without fear or menace. It was a world without end, without bombs or terror, the kind everyone seeks again and again. Until the late summer evening when they gave the big party.

Everyone was invited. I got to the party at seven, the country time for parties to start, and saw their house standing cool and friendly and, for that instant, strangely vacant looking in the haze of twilight. There was a sense of abatement about it, as if something had stopped—the moment of tranquil hesitation before a party leaps into life.

Then all at once it did begin. Cows lowed from the barn, sounding like part of the party, and Ed came out of the milkshed that had been fixed up like a pavilion with bars along two sides. He was wearing light blue tropical-worsted slacks and a hand-stitched, expensive soft gray jacket, and looked tall and movie-ish again, and was grinning with the hidden excitement he always got from parties.

Everything began popping at once. Cars scrunched into the driveway. A bass horn kept practicing a *humpha-humpha* that sounded like some mourning bird, but came from a corner of the long screened porch where there was going to be dancing— they had hired the local five-piece band. Bud Devere, who was

going to be bartender, popped from the kitchen, white-
aproned, and slamming the door, disappeared into the milkshed
pavilion. Lights went on—darkness seemed to fall all at once,
not like usual summer twilights when day lingers. Ed had flood-
lighted the sides of the house and the milkshed with blue and
amber spots. There was a silky laugh from inside the house and
Paulie came out to greet people. It was an inside-outside party.
The lawns, porches, milkshed, and the whole house were uti-
lized; and, before the party ended, some of the concealing
shrubbery as well by the spirited young. Children came to the
party too, yelling, crashing into things, racing across lawns,
screaming back to harbor among their mothers' knees.

"Oh, where's Ed?" Paulie asked. "Someone's got to carry
the punch out to the porch—the ladies' punch." Someone car-

ried the punch out. Paulie followed like a nervous, laughing bird. Tonight she wasn't wearing an actual babushka, but one of thin tan lace. "This? It was on one of my mother's dresses." It made her face even smaller, nose and chin and cheekbones chiseled like the head of a miniature. "Oh, who's going to light the candles?" Someone lit the candles. "Well, who's going to dance? Someone start the dancing!" Several young couples began the dancing. "Oh, there's Aunt Dell!"

A huge second-hand limousine pulled into the driveway and agilely lined itself up in between the other cars, a big black beetle nuzzling in between more beetles, and Aunt Dell, surrounded by her family, came hugely enjoying herself from the car. All her family pouring out looked like the circus trick of dozens of clowns overflowing from a single auto. Aunt Dell also brought baked hams that Paulie had asked her to roast. Later, when it was sliced, Paulie kept chattering in her toy-flute voice, seeing that even the shyest children had their plates kept filled.

"Oh!" Paulie beckoned to me. She held a heaped plate, and smiled; but also the troubled wings under her eyes were darker. "Where's Walter Cwym? Will you find him? He's always so scared at parties." She put the plate in my hand and motioned me off.

Walter was sitting in the old porch swing, far behind the house, where none of the colored lights could reach him. We swung back and forth, while Walter ate.

"Something's wrong with Paulie," he said abruptly.

"Something wrong? Nothing except that she's having the time of her life. She's happiest taking care of everyone—a big brood hen."

"Party's too big," Walter said calmly. "Too noisy. She never hired a band before."

"Ed can afford it."

"Something's wrong with Ed, too."

By that time, the Kootz boys had started their fight. Like many country fights, it had no particular beginning or end—it was only the middle that counted. It was born only of the sheer joy country people find in walloping, swinging, jabbing, flinging themselves aimlessly, spinning, sprawling, bleeding, cursing, muttering, and suddenly combing their hair and buying each other drinks again. The fight started on the drive, the Kootz boys bludgeoning it out with Sam Breadlow and someone I didn't know, men running from the pavilion, women hollering for their children from the screened porch, other men

looking as if they would gladly get into the fight but didn't quite know whom to hit, so they started their own fights on the sidelines, and then Ed's long angry arm pulling them apart and walloping a few himself to bring their senses back and suddenly Paulie in between the Kootz boys, her face wild with rage, eyes flashing, voice plinking in fury, her small fingers pecking at them like little beaks—but, nevertheless, halting the fight.

"Please," she demanded. "Oh, stop it, will you?" Not pleading, but incensed. "What's wrong with you?" In the flashing light she looked a hundred years old, but beautiful. The green, amber, and blue lights Ed had installed made funny eerie shadows over the drive, and every shadow was magnified a dozen times. The Kootzes blushed bloodily but looked sheepish. "If you want to fight go to your own land, boys. But not at my party—please, can't I have it a good party?" She had taken out her handkerchief, but was laughing suddenly, dabbing at Bill Kootz's eyelid, and the laugh was like a cooling shower on all the tempers. "Bill Kootz, come on dance with me. There's nothing wrong with my dancing, is there?"

She danced, as a matter of fact, very well, her feet spinning swiftly over the painted porch floor. Next she danced with the other Kootz boy. It became a cheerful, loud, yet well-mannered party again. There was no punishment in Paulie.

Unexpectedly, Ed was standing behind me. We were just becoming good friends. He watched Paulie spinning in Duke Kootz's arms in front of all the grinning, ample women with children in their laps.

"She's a wonderful woman," Ed said softly.

He looked scared.

"Is something wrong with you?" I asked.

"Nothing a good drink won't cure," he laughed, and steered me out to the pavilion.

Ed and Paulie stood together out on the lawn as the party ended, his arms around her shoulders like a shawl against the cooling night. They laughed as they said good-by to each guest and Ed kissed the ladies. No one could believe how, after the last guest had gone, they could shut the never-locked door of their house, lock it, see no one again, speak to almost no one except when Ed had business to tend to with a neighbor, never entertain again, never go fishing unless alone and unannounced, and then not to the lakes they knew but to faraway lakes where they were not known, never answer their telephone except guardedly, never accept another invitation to visit neighbor or friend, never to help a neighbor, though these refusals came with the great civility and decency that nothing could kill in Paulie; nor in Ed, as if through absorption he had acquired it from her. They simply absented themselves from life —or so it seemed, but really they lived it more hungrily, neither giving up his staggering reverence for it. I would see Ed over a fence line while walking in the woods, or Paulie, while shopping in the village, and outwardly they had not changed since that one unexpected summer evening of curtain-drawing. Each said a few words, smiled, looked me straight in the eye.

But then they walked away again. They lived in some terrible, vacuous silence. They were polite ghosts. They withdrew as if countryside and neighbors and friends had committed a shame against them, but one they accepted without anger or resentment. They even repainted their house one summer, but hired a painter from a town thirty miles away instead of their cleft-palated friend, Emlyn Jarvis, from the village.

It was not the angry hermit's life I had lived in my first year.

It was only that a sign had gone up on their lives: KEEP OUT. With the party they had paid up their debts, and let everyone know how fond they were of them, before withdrawing. I saw Paulie out at their gate one day. She was only winding a trumpet vine around the post, but she might have been putting up the sign, the knotted ends of her babushka flapping, stretching as high as she could to nail up the invisible warning. Ed stood protectively beside her.

I stopped the car. "How're things going?"

"Oh, fine," Paulie laughed.

Ed grinned at me. "Been fishing? How they biting?"

"No, I haven't. How'd you both like to go sometime?"

"They're supposed to be biting at Schoolteacher Lake," Paulie said vaguely, leaning against Ed. "You ought to try there."

"Or Fowler Lake. Ever try there?" Ed said.

Neither seemed to have heard my invitation that they go along. They both walked inside their gate. But they did not glower from behind their sign. They watched me with a kindly distraction, a sense of wishing that they might ask me in but, well yes, it was just better if they didn't. No hurt feelings. Paulie picked up a few pebbles, sighing her high laughter, and playfully tossed them into my car. Without warning, I saw Ed's face go gray under his handsome tan and he looked away and swallowed, but when he turned back again he was still grinning. Their whole story is common knowledge now. Oh, the song of life and the land, and Paulie's song, and Ed's, it was sad and beautiful to learn and to hear.

6

And Neighbors in the Night

BUT before I heard the end of it, there were other neighbors
to meet and grow fond of. The apple-orcharding Pelhams.
Zodiac Orchards. Mrs. Pelham was an astrologist and pruned
and picked by the moon, which meant that one year all their
apples, bushel on bushel lined up in the sheds, were still hard
and green. But when the moon is on their side, the Pelhams
grow the biggest, juiciest apples anyone has ever seen.

Which Walter Cwym can't do, who sat on the lawn swing
with me that one night. He was from near Genesee and his passion was his vegetable stand, freshly painted each year or sometimes twice, like a fair booth or a child's play store, gleaming
and bright. But the land was not with him. He did not love it
enough. He would neglect his fields to spruce up his store on
the highway, and all the earth would produce for him was
rickety vegetables and flowers, aphidy broccoli, peas hard as
BB shot, thrippy gladioli, wormy apples and kernelless corn
that grinned its surprise like a toothless mouth when the husk
was pulled back.

For more neighbors, there were the doctors and nurses and sometimes a patient from the State tubercular sanitarium a half mile away, like the one whose wife came up from the South to be near him, and stayed a year and a half, and out of boredom became a drunkard while she waited, so that by the time he was released *she* had become the patient—but he left her behind, too eager for the outside world to wait for her. And there were Buck Fife and his family and the unexpected party I gave for them one evening.

Again there was the inborn courtesy and reticence—the circling around and sniffing to see who would make the first overture—that had kept the surrounding neighbors aloof at the beginning, suspecting my own indifference to them, nodding to me when they met me but with no more recognition than they might give a penguin or Bushman. While he was building the house, Joe would come out with his family on summer Sundays to picnic in the woods (love already had him even then) and occasionally, he said, a cluster of young girls would come strolling up the meadow from nowhere, sometimes more than a dozen of them, to look around in silence for a while and then go away again. But nothing more. It satisfied me. I wanted no visiting neighbors.

As yet, by the second summer, no party had ever taken place inside my house. The many friends I had planned would visit me during the lazy summers—the bright-faced, well-dressed city visitors laughing on the terraces, roaming in the gardens, fishing in the stream or hunting in the woods—not one of these had yet appeared. The late afternoon silence over the terrace rarely had been shattered by the clink of a glass or convivial laughter of a friend. No one walked down to the iris patch along the fence, except myself. The trout slept undisturbed in the shade of rocks in the stream. Gunfire never made the leaves of the pin oak lift and rustle in alarm. The house itself remained only a house. Because I had come to want no friends inside these very four walls I had raised to harbor friends.

So the party that night with the Fifes was by way of being unanticipatedly baptismal. Down at the Corners in the slapdash Festive Country Club, the night was less festive than usual. A young farm couple was there, their six-months-old-baby bundled and asleep atop the pinball machine. There was no singing of Welsh hymns that night. It was a sleepy night, when you know nothing is going to happen—the inaction hangs in the air like smoke, curling around the pendent lights in lazy wisps of nothing. Someone finally came in and wanted to play the pinball machine so the baby had to be lifted off and put to sleep on the bar for a while, but soon it woke up, sore and yelling, and then the young couple got sore at the baby and left, taking it along, of course. The pinball player shot a few more games, tilted the machine, which made Chris, the bartender, who wouldn't cheat at solitaire, get sore and start yelling at the player. The player got sore and walked out. It was the kind of evening when such things would keep happening, people appearing and vanishing, no one talking much, a somnolence over the countryside, as well as an unsounded augury of topsy-turviness that made you think even the oats must be growing upside down. I remember now there was no moon.

Buck Fife came in just before one o'clock closing time. He is strong and wiry and works for the county, hauling gravel in summer and jamming a snow plow in winter against the clogged county roads. During the previous winter of my isolation he had cleared the road up to the house twice after blizzards, good-naturedly ramming his plow down the lane and spewing up shivering waves of snow on either side, leaving the roadbed clean and flat, though since this was a private road he should not have been there at all. He just had a helpful streak. But he didn't give any particular sign of recognition when he came in that night. I looked at him down the long bar and nodded. He nodded back, but not smiling—a kind of brush-off. Then a boilermaker was set in front of me. "Buck," Chris said, nodding down the bar. I looked at Buck, picked up my glass, and nodded. Buck nodded back solemnly. No foolish words. You would have thought the place was so packed and noisy you couldn't have heard them anyway.

It was one o'clock and I couldn't buy back. "Why don't you stop up at the house for a nightcap?"

Buck didn't exactly smile in answer, but almost. "Sure. I've got my car."

I went home, waited ten, fifteen, twenty minutes for Buck to show up, until it grew plain he wasn't coming after all. There had been no one down at the Corners but Buck and myself, and it was nearly one-thirty now—every house for as far as could be seen from the black hilltop was equally black with sleep. The blackness stretched far down the meadow. It was time to turn out the yardlight and the lamps and go to bed. But then a pair of headlights flashed down at the gateway. Then a pilgrimage of cars turned into the driveway and up the hill as might have cluttered the European roads of retreat.

How they communicated, connived with, and collected each other in such short time and in dead of night must have been part of the night's moonless enchantment. Buck's parents came. His brothers. Their wives. His sisters. Their husbands. The children of both. Buck's girl. *Her* parents. And some of *their* neighbors' kids.

"Well," Buck said at the door. "Myrt couldn't come. She's got summer grippe. Says she'll make it some other time." He really smiled. "Nice of you to ask us up. Sometimes city guys move out here and act stuck-up."

I had no (and still haven't) idea who Myrt was (but hope she's better) but there were women there with only coats thrown over their pajamas; out in the cars at least four children, evidently not yet party-size, slept on the back seats, ripped from their beds as from a fire. I looked for the couple with the pinball baby, but they must have been still sore and hadn't come.

Buck found me opening and slamming car doors. It was fas-

cinating to see what might be asleep inside. "Looking for something?"

"Just for a baby."

"Plenty inside," Buck said.

"Ba-*bee*, not babe."

"Wow. Have a slug?" Buck held out a pint of whisky, his
grin perpetual now.

"Well, not a straight one. Let's go mix a round of highballs."

The party was really a good one. People sat around stiffly at
first, looking doubtful about whether they should have come,
the men tending to segregate themselves from their women as
if disclaiming kinship. There were tentative offers of conversation, less friendly from the young than from the old, and
everyone wore a look of wondering what in the world they were
doing there, and what strange, wild compulsion had routed
them from their beds. Their half-awake, half-unreal faces still
seemed to be hearing a telephone jangling through the night,
clarioning out its order to scramble into their clothes and get
going. There was not unfriendliness. But massive uncertainties
and grave doubts flooded the house.

These were in part the famed teetotalling Welsh. But when
the drinks were brought out they took them gingerly, their faces
shut as doors, and with an air of doing their expected duties
downed them like cokes. But the drinks helped. So did music.
The sisters-in-law and brothers-in-law began dancing with each
other, while the parents sat around in chairs laughing politely
like parents at a dancing school, but certainly a peculiar dancing school because by now one of Buck's brothers-in-law, wearing Mrs. Fife's kerchief around his head, was dancing with
Buck's unmarried sister May who kept coaxing him to throw
her over his head. And, not at any distinct moment, not at any
special time, no one could have said at what exact instant it

happened, I had been incorporated into their world. It was exhilarating to see one family having so much fun. All of them laughed their heads off at some of the modern paintings on the wall.

"You shoulda brought some of your costumes along, May," Buck called to his sister.

"I know I shoulda," May yelled back.

"You should see May in some of her costumes," Buck said to me.

"I'd like to," I said.

"Wow. Next time," Buck said.

Some of the women went to the kitchen and made thick sandwiches of ham and rye bread. No one told them to, but someone accidentally found the ham. They just happened to be looking into the icebox. It was a specially smoked ham.

"That's a Virginia ham," I said.

"Ham's ham," Buck's mother smiled.

They worked efficiently and sliced the whole ham into sandwiches, spread thick with mustard. Someone happened to be looking through the cupboards and found pickles and olives, so we had them too. They chuckled over the size of the kitchen. They said I must be going to get married or why'd I have a sink and stove and so many cupboards and everything put in. Then they shrieked for Estelle, who someone said was another of Buck's unmarried sisters, and everyone went to look for her. But when they found her, sorting through my neckties in the bedroom, she gracefully turned out to be only nine years old.

And the men, all the older men who weren't dancing, went around thumping the walls. Nice job, they said, must've had a good builder. Solid. No cheap stuff. Good wood. So this is what the place looks like, everyone began saying and grinning. One of Buck's brothers-in-law was practicing to be an amateur magician and had brought his rabbit along and after a few drinks kept losing it. "My husband lost his rabbit," his wife murmured politely, and everyone went hopping after it under the beds and behind the commode and in closets, but in that way everyone got a thorough look at the house. They liked the house. They all stayed until five o'clock in the morning when the babies in the cars began to wake up. People went home happy and tired as after a wedding.

All except Buck, who passed out on the sofa and had to stay the blue-gray remainder of the night. In the morning when I woke him he nodded at me solemnly but without any real recognition, more with sullen suspicion, and I nodded back solemnly, and then he left. Just like in the movies, though, he marched through the bathroom door first, then a bedroom door, then a closet door. I had to show him the right door out and we both nodded again. Then he got into his car and drove straight through a rose bed and down the meadow. I had to run after him and turn him around toward the road, and waited to nod again but he wouldn't and was gone.

I was sorry he wouldn't turn and wave. Because the house at last had had a party. It looked warmer and bigger, when I went inside.

7

The Roots

I GRADUALLY came to know, and care, that I was back in the land where my grandfather had been born. New York seemed farther and farther away, now that I had friends, was making a life. I still would return to New York, almost any day now. I was strong enough to grapple again, my humor was back. I got train schedules. I wrote letters of application to New York agencies. I received cordial answers and sent them cordial answers in return. I set a date to return; made an appointment with the most cordial of the answerees. The date just slipped by. I wrote a note of apology, was urged to set another date. Soon, I would. . . .

But I was occupied with small things, which seemed to erase the big things from my mind. I was busy remembering things. As a boy I had visited my grandfather in these hills, picnicked with my father and mother in the groves. My grandfather, whom I thought I remembered nothing about, grew alive again. And much that the boy, who was myself, had taught me began to come back to me now. The names of flowers growing alongside the bog or in high dry places, the names of tools and implements, the adze and disc, the smell of wild cucumber in blossom, the feel of dirt sighing through the fingers, the winey fragrance of the elderberry and the fainter, softer taste of the wine it made.

Until now I had been rootless, because roots will not take hold in the dry caked earth of Verdi Square. But now the stars shining over my head were in the right positions again, not seen from alien slants. Looking up at them I could feel a boundless continuity I had never known before, or even known I wanted. I felt a power of possibilities inside me. I recognized, dimly at first, but then with certainty, that this was the opposite of what I had felt when I looked up at high buildings: that I was nothing, expendable and confined. The aching, sleepless nights, the panicky dreams, the tearing nerves—they had been part of the nothingness.

And I learned to love the land, and the new house on it. I even began to want a name for the house—as one wants to know the intimate name of a new acquaintance whom one suspects one might grow to love. The need rose mysteriously, out of some hidden, vague respect and contentment. By naming houses, farms, our acreage in life, we lay claim to them, somehow everlastingly, and there is the sense of continuity again that you never can find in city places, and better still if that name, the anchor, appears by itself with as little effort as roots sliding in searching silence beneath the earth.

So the name came—without being asked to, or anyone looking for it or even acquiescing, and as simply as a bird learns its notes. I heard it first in our village grocery, an honest and plain store where meats, cough drops, tools, paint, falling-hair remedies, overalls, pickles, *Ladies' Home Journals*, paper-backed books, rock candy, hard sugar candies at Christmas, that I hadn't seen for twenty years—the kind with a design inside like that in paperweights—are all heaped together on the shelves and counter. (The Christmas decoration is a red tissue paper bell hung from the ceiling, and it looks prettier than the thousand bells at Macy's and its faded single clapper seems to ring much louder.) It is a wonderful, heartbreaking place to shop. Soupbones still are free. When you buy Arm & Hammer's baking soda, you still expect to find the bird pictures in the box. You are safe here, near your youth and remembered places. Time goes slow here, all right, but each minute is fuller. There I first heard the name.

A can of porch paint, a pork roast, a bag of onions still smelling of the dirt they came from, were piled on the counter but because I was going on into town, I asked to have them sent up to the house.

"He wants this stuff delivered," Harry, the grocer, said to his boy.

"Where to?" the boy said. Then he glanced at me. "Oh. Up there." ·

"Y Ty d'r y Bryn," Harry said.

The boy nodded.

"What's that?" I asked.

"Y Ty d'r y Bryn," Harry said.

"I heard you, but what is it?"

"Don't you know your own place? Y Ty d'r y Bryn," Harry said. "House on the hill. Where you live."

The Welsh do that. Not unlike the Indians did, they call their neighbors The Man Who Lives In The Valley or Man With The Apple Trees or The Man On The Big Hill. And I lived in Y Ty d'r y Bryn. The House On The Hill. It wasn't the kind of name I was looking and waiting for. And I'm not Welsh. But the name had happened. It *was*. Then neighbors who weren't Welsh simply began translating it. Oh, it's you from up at the House on the Hill. Well, how are things going up at the House on the Hill? Perhaps it sounds ineffectual, but in Welsh it has a flavor. Anyway, now no one could change it, for the name has wound its own roots around the rocks and trees and the whole existence of the land.

It felt wonderful. I'd been located. You name every small piece of earth you can set foot on. You find your bearings that way. All this I learned. You find continuity. It gives a family feeling. You want other men to know you have been some-where, that the earth didn't swallow you without leaving some mark on it. You give names to sink your own roots or to have a trunk to hang on to. Old Mary Lowry, the mail carrier's wife who got her B.A. in biology, says, "You take every wild flower, beetle, moth, spider, fish, fowl, tree, vine, herb, and mark it with your own name, way back as far as Linnaeus. Nature doesn't give a hoot about you but that way it makes it seem she at least cared." Dr. Aplin, in Genesee Depot, says, "We sign our names even to the diseases that kill us—Bright's, Parkin-son's." Ironic signposts left behind us for when we are gone.

But there is great comfort in this passion for names bestowed unthinkingly, the anchoring roots sent deep. The hills and hol-lows around the house, easily, naturally, acquired place names without anyone knowing it, and it made the hills and hollows seem closer. We were friends, recognizing each other, able to call to each other—they were offering warmth and comfort. We will always encircle and remember you, the hills said. Again, the desire to call these places by a name, as you might a friend, returned, and subconsciously must have created the names. But in another way, the names just happened in the same way that a new friend comes to you already owning a name by which you will call him. You don't name your friend—you merely learn to recognize the one he already has.

Sloping down from the kitchen side of the house toward the railroad track, with a few old apple trees still remembering to bear a few apples each year, was a piece of land that soon identified itself as the Old Place. No one said, We ought to call this the Old Place. A few, tired, slow trains each day chug by it, and the train itself seems to be grinding and whistling its way out of the safe past. Down at the foot of the steep hill are the remains of a fieldstone foundation where the original homestead stood on this land a hundred years ago. There is a juniper, great and scraggly now, at each corner of the collapsed foundation, and bent senile lilacs in between. Hop vines still grow along the fence—decades ago, the Welsh countrywomen made their "rising" from hops. And golden yarrow where the kitchen dooryard must have been. The yarrow has spread into a dense patch and the hops have jumped from fence to stumps and there is an unutterable disconsolation about the fallen walls of the house on autumn afternoons. Friends and neighbors began to speak of it as the Old Place, not by design but as if each secretly heard his own kind of imagined voices speaking there. Each seemed to make a silent journey into his own past, to be going back home, remembering where he came from, without which remembrance no one can ever go forward.

On the hill to the west of the Old Place are dozens of small junipers, from a few inches to six feet tall, that have seeded themselves from the four parent trees around the ruined foundation, stirring proof, again, of the continuousness of nature of which the entire countryside is always reminding you. My mother, out for a stroll through these memory-laden hills, while the house was being built, spoke with the delight in her voice

that is always in a city woman's, who was country-born, at re-
discovering the free and nourishing gifts, the fruits and berries,
the small ripe joys, that fill the woods and open fields. Tin pail
in hand as she climbed the hill, I was reminded of the picture
she conjured up whenever she told how, long ago, on first moving to a city from a log cabin up north, her German father
would send her with a tin pail down to the corner saloon for
his suppertime can of beer, into which on wintry days he dipped
a red hot poker from the coal stove to lift the chill. Tin pail in
hand she climbed again, much older now, slower than in her
girlhood's dash to the corner, up the hill among the low junipers, all the way up to the top where she had found a tangle of
wild red raspberries. Her rediscovery was similar to mine,
though far more real, for in her childhood the finding of berries and nuts was a vital part of sustenance—berries to preserve,
sumac pods to make ink, nuts from which to grind oil. Now she
found the berries again just as she had found them half a century ago on other hills. She came down the hill with a look of
grave astonishment on her face.

"I'm glad you left New York. I think you're going to find
something out here Pa and I both had when we were kids—I
don't know what exactly. But a kind of gratitude. Look at all
these berries, for instance. Juniper Hill is covered with them,
just waiting to be picked—"

You're going to find something out here, a kind of gratitude
. . . but something else rang through her words, unwittingly
became fixed, a sound as lasting as stone. A new name had come
unbidden. Juniper Hill. No one had ever called it that before.
Perhaps even, at that time, it meant little to me. But later it
became another place name to come back to, a hill to remember no matter how far away I went, an anchor in time and space.
A place to feel grateful.

There were other names—the Grotto, a deep pothole with a high growth of trees so dense, so dark, that there is no underbrush, no foliage on the trees up to a height of twenty or thirty feet along their trunks, and this hidden place has such a sobering religious air about it that John Thomas, our preacher, said we ought to build a grotto there. When the world was destroyed, he laughed, he could still hold secret services in it. But I noticed he kept his fingers crossed as he said it, and uncannily now I find myself doing the same when I walk there. And there were still other names—the Back Pasture, Hepatica Hill, Dog Hollow, this last a name donated by Tom.

Tom is one of Aunt Dell's children, not the kiddo Buss who so rightly deserves to be straggled, but a sane and reasonable twelve-year-old—he is the favored mirror of her commodious soul.

He is part of the woods and roams in them constantly. Soon after I moved out here it became clear that these hills and kettles could never belong only to the person who owned the deed to them—too many neighbors and their parents and before them their parents, over the last century, have hunted rabbits and coons and partridge in them and hollered through them in winter, picked the wildflowers in spring, wild plums, red and black raspberries, fat blackberries in summer, for these hills ever to belong to one person. I relinquished them long ago; neighbors hunt or sled down the icy hills or make love in them as they please; and always, somewhere in them, is Tom.

He can go barefooted where a dog would flinch. He is, as a matter of fact, a typical country boy-and-his-dog boy, because a half-dozen strays are always following him. In the woods, he has an eye as quick as his wiry body, and a need to protect things. There is a dell-like formation beyond the Juniper Hill, a circular enclosure rimmed by plum and crab, pink and white in the springtime. The hush there is as tangible as water. One day in the dell Tom found something I had not noticed before. A freshly cut rectangle, its edges straight as a ruler, in the green sod. It was frightening, like a new grave, and so small. The sod had been lifted and carefully replaced. We began to guess what was under it—a dismembered murder victim, a burglar's haul, someone's dog. We never disturbed the sod to find out. Tom walked around it carefully and in silence, with the wonderful regard and respect children will sometimes have for unknown things. His thin lips were dry. One of his stray friends was sniffing and whimpering at the edges of the plot.

"If someone liked his dog enough to bring him out here and bury him and cover him up so careful, then I don't think we—" Tom looked up at me.

"Sure."

His glance was grateful. The plot of ground was to remain unmolested. He stamped a corner with his bare heel where the sod needed tamping—he took good care of it. Perhaps this was the gratitude my mother had said you learned in the country among natural things. At any rate, Tom always has an instinct to protect, to help, to restore nests to trees, to release animals from traps. I thought he had forgotten the buried dog as we walked on through the woods, two or three live dogs following him, leaping on him and urging him along with such vital impatience. He tested a hazel thicket to see if the nuts were swelling in their crinkled pale green pods, and dug up a small piece of quartz with his fingernails, and began to argue loudly and hotly with me about the Waldeens' peculiar withdrawal, which had lasted for nearly a year by then—he joins freely and with innate intelligence in adult gossip. (Later his theory, or hunch, or kid's wild guess, or whatever it was, proved right.) We had

reached the far edge of the woods, when we both looked up. There was Paulie Waldeen.

She looked startled, the babushka-framed face smiling as if to cover some embarrassment, but perhaps nothing more than that she was mooning along through somebody else's woods (when she tended her own KEEP OUT sign so vigilantly), but beyond the smile in her bright, dark-winged eyes was the same frigid isolation. It is a look you see often on city streets, but not one you expect to find in the country, in the woods, under a benevolent umbrella of sheltering oaks. Nothing in Tom let on that we had been talking about her and Ed's disappearance from our lives. Tom slid a friendly, brown, scratched arm around her waist.

"Paulie, we found a new grave."

Paulie made a face, the small features crinkling together, squeezed up like a rag doll's head—she loves life, I reminded myself, but I know now that her face went white, even though in the shadowed woods it seemed that no more than a ripple passed over it. "A grave? Whose?" her flute's voice said. She looked up at me, laughing, and absently let her fingers rumple Tom's hair.

"Somebody's dog is in it. You know anyone lost his dog, or it got shot?" Tom asked.

"Oh no! Somebody's dog? Where is it?" Her fear passed, and Paulie was all concern and pity.

Tom pointed backward. "In the Dog Hollow." No one had ever called it that before. He named it without thinking—now everyone knows where the Dog Hollow is.

Tom led Paulie back toward the Dog Hollow, and both of them set to work covering the small plot with twigs and old leaves, lest someone else find it and disturb it out of curiosity. When she had finished, Paulie gave me a strained smile, straightened up, and blinked around the dell somewhat like a bird blinking abstractedly, yet alert for dangers every instant. "How's Ed?" I asked. "Ed?" She looked at me sharply. "Why, Ed's all right. He's got to be." All at once her slight, thin body was knotted into a preposterous rigidity of strength and she was glaring at me, but half in appeal, too, as if I were something which she must annihilate but at the same time concede to. "*Oh, he's got to be!*" But in another instant, it—whatever "it" was—vanished. She had accepted something. I thought I was beginning to understand the closing of their doors, as she stood there, talking a while longer, admiring the piece of quartz Tom fished out to show her, little spots of red spinning on her cheeks, turning the quartz over in her fragile fingers, then saying good-by to us cheerfully and politely and starting back toward her own fence line, so small that the hazelnut shrubs were taller than she. But she was also as strong as any tree, sapling or giant, that grew in the woods.

"She's funny," Tom said.

"I know."

"I like her."

"So do I."

"Do you think Ed's sick?"

"I don't know." I thought a moment. "You wouldn't think so, seeing him work in the fields."

"You never can tell, though."

"I know it."

"She whispered something to me."

"What?"

"When we were fooling around in the Dog Hollow. 'I never saw a wild thing sorry for itself.'"

"That's D. H. Lawrence."

"Who's he?"

"An English writer. You know, you're a creator yourself."

"Why?"

"You just named that pothole. Dog Hollow."

"What else would you call it?"

I laughed, but also felt a kind of jubilance. I wanted to clap Tom's back and cry, Of course, what else would you call it? It was so right. I felt a gratitude for this gift Tom had given the earth: a name. It would always be more important now, and have continuity, an identity, an anchor. Only remembering Paulie kept me quiet.

We came out of the woods and sat down to rest at the Old Place. From neighbors and relatives Tom has collected old stories about the crumbled house and about the first family that lived in it a century ago, struggling wretchedly to feed even itself, let alone cattle, from this rocky, barren, glacial soil— the mullen and sheep sorrel, all that will grow in the big meadow even now, years afterward, are silent testimony to that —and about the wife of that family who, one fall, took a job shucking corn with the farmer to the south of her. Down in the old house the husband grew suddenly ill, and started after his wife for help, but he got no farther than the top of the hill, where the new house stands now, when he fell lifeless. The woman with her children lived alone after that, planting her yarrow, tending the hops vines, until the house passed into other hands. No one knows where the woman went to or where or how she died. She isn't there anymore but her yarrow is, the hops, lilacs, and junipers, and the new junipers wandering up over the neighboring hill now like green everlasting promises of immortality. So in a way the woman is still there too. From Tom's silence, I know he knew this, too.

You have a funny feeling, sitting and looking at the empty

foundation of the old house, which all at once is not empty at all. Beside you sits the boy you once were. Time gets mixed up, moving backward and forward. The rocks and mortar, the yarrow patch, the pump rusty from disuse, the deep-rooted lilacs, are not unlike those you remember from around your grandfather's house. Space gets mixed up, too. Up above you stands the new house, white and calm with its solid black roof. You're there, and you aren't. You look around you. There is silence to hear what you want to hear, not subway rumblings or feet on cement or shrieking horns, but the whirr of a partridge or a last year's dry leaf spinning like a solitary pinwheel high up on a tree limb, or just nothing. And there is air to breathe. There is the sudden, pleasant exhaustion of having been on a journey and come back home. No matter where you go, there is this place now to return to.

8

The Dill Crock

ALL I know is that the second summer waned; September came and then October and then November. I got my bags out again, along with the train schedule. A faint homesickness for the city began—for good restaurants, theaters, music that I could actually see being played.

Friends wrote to ask why I was burying myself in the country. I wondered too, until it occurred to me that one could be buried just as well in a high building. Hadn't I been? I told myself I ought to return to cities to refresh myself politically. But weren't politics argued just as heatedly and wisely, or unwisely, down at the Festive Country Club? Didn't we elect the same President?

But I ought to see what was happening in the world. My heart answered at once—was this less a world? But I ought to meet *people*. Oh? Were Bud Devere, Aunt Dell, the Waldeens, Walter Cwym, the Fifes, less than flesh and blood?

One day an ad appeared in our local paper:

WANTED TO RENT: *City resident will pay $300 down immediately against rental of room in farm or village home, to be occupied in event of atomic war. Will forfeit, if no bomb. Write J.R. Box 120.*

J.R. seemed a piteously trapped and jittery soul. Was three hundred dollars his life savings? Was he casting it all away on a gamble for safety? Was the countryside such a haven, after all? But more than that kept me here, because with half the world destroyed, the country would be no better place to live. Rather, it was the increasing need—increasing inside me mysteriously—to learn something else before a bomb might fall. It was a need I had not known ever existed in me. (Out of it the aching, racing, sleepless nights had come unwittingly?) That need was growing fearful. Should earth vanish, I wanted at least to know I had been on earth. Out of my anger, I had learned that this was what I needed and wanted most to know.

I had already learned that there was enough life in a square mile in the country to make a nation. And I was not trapped here any longer, or perishing in resentment and remorse. So I could find no real reason for leaving.

By staying, I had so much to gain. I had time, space, silence, air to breathe. I had things to look at, things to feel. In September, every tree in the woods became a Circe. Maples were a golden smoky haze that you felt you looked through, rather than at. Sumacs covered entire hillsides, orange to red to scarlet. As well as the bright colors, there were the delicate ones I had never noticed before. The new growth of raspberry canes became a ghostly pink. The fluff in which wind anemone seeds were carried, floating to make new stands, were a cloudlike silver. Columbine leaves were mauve.

The seed pods of weeds and wildflowers became flowerlike

forms that looked made of wood or thinnest tissue or shaved of stone, every pod or dead grass stalk with its own intricate design and texture. Parts of me got tangled in the creeping fire of the woodbine vine. In the meadow stood the tall darting stalks of the dark brown mullein, the huge curled silver-spotted wild tobacco leaves. Along fences around the Old Place was the brittle, crepelike pink and tan bloom of hops. Ice formed like thinnest lace on ponds. The hills settled, seemed to curl, sleep. I would see all this and feel the retreat from cities growing still stronger inside me. Christina Rossetti found a day in the country worth a month in town, and as I kept telling myself I ought to go pack a suitcase, I was repeating her words instead.

But there was another, and simpler, reason. Something unexpected had happened, as it happened to Joe while he built the house. It was that I was in love. I was in love with Aunt Dell and with Millie and Carrie Litten. And with Tom and the Waldeens and Buck Fife and his gang down at the Festive Country Club. With our postmistress and the girl who played kettle drums in the local symphony orchestra in a town eight miles away. With cows, ovenbirds, homemade bread, these acres, downy gentians that I had never seen before. With having time to think, sawing wood for the kitchen fireplace, making wine from wild grapes. With reading late at night, instead of running to the midnight show of the newsreel theater on Verdi Square because I could not sleep or think of anything else to do. With sleeping, and with waking up, feeling awake. With getting a dog named Shag and with planting a thousand multiflora roses, provided free by an alert State Conservation Department, down the edges of the meadow and along bounding hillsides for new fencerows. And with a dill crock.

A dill crock may not be so remarkable unless one has an Aunt Dell to reveal its mysteries. She raced up one late August day,

stepped down several feet from her huge high car and broke
into a flashing smile.

"You got you a crock?" she demanded. "A good big one?"
Without waiting for an answer she opened the rear door of
her car, like a burly chauffeur opening the tonneau for a
duchess to step out, only the duchess turned into an enormous
bunch of pungent fresh dill, plus a fistful of faded and twisted
daylilies already closing for the night (hadn't I said she will
only grow the evanescent in her flower garden?), plus baskets of
various produce, plus a five-gallon earthenware crock.

"But anyhow I brought you one," she said, pointing at the
crock. "I got me so many crocks, I said to myself you just drag
one along up the hill." She beamed enthusiastically.

"Swell," I said. "I'm glad you did. Glad to see you, too."

"No kidding, ainna?" she answered, and glanced at me admiringly, as if I had said something very wise and to the point.
She ducked into the back of the car again, reappearing with a
bushel basket full of small fat pickling cucumbers. "We got
these cukes by the galore in the garden. I said to myself, Look
all them poor cukes laying there," her eyes went misty at the
plight of the poor abandoned cukes, "I'll just take some along
up the hill, too."

"*Muchas gracias.*"

"Don't talk Welsh, mister. I'm no Welshman. Grab that
basket there under below the bottom and help carry her inside."

She was all busy, solid energy. I grabbed the bushel basket of
cucumbers under below the bottom as directed and helped her
lug it into the kitchen. I know Aunt Dell could have carried
the basket alone, though the handles were broken off, but she
had the five-gallon crock in the other hand. And the crock was
half filled with green beans.

She took over the kitchen, washed up dishes left from lunch, put up a big kettle of water to boil, dumped in the green beans, and initiated me into the wonder of a dill crock. Since then, a dill crock is what makes every summer morning worth waking up to—everyone *needs* a dill crock. August is not August anymore without one and the reluctant vegetable plot has been composted and coaxed into producing at least a sound patch of dill each year, as well as a smattering of those vegetables that swim so amicably in their dill bath.

"Ain't never had a dill crock before, mister?" Aunt Dell asked with a shake of her head. She struggled to pull herself together after such a blow. "Just you toss me into the pot some garlic—a good handful, see?"

I peeled garlic cloves, a fistful, and tossed them into the crock. (And what has such a look of stolid comfort, and such a feel of everlasting providence, as a good-sized earthenware crock sitting in one's kitchen?) Aunt Dell parboiled the green beans, but not one instant more than five minutes, "just to get the fuzz taste off them things," she said, then drained the beans and flung them, I do not doubt with incantations, into the crock. I love to watch Aunt Dell cook. She measures and flips and dips and scoops and rinses and fills and empties and never stops talking for a second all at the same time, and it would seem no part of her body or brain could possibly know what the other part is doing, but what comes out, the finished product, is always as complete and hearty as Aunt Dell herself.

"Hear my kiddo Tom's been up here hanging around your woods. Nice kiddo," she sighed—a lusty, heartfelt sigh, as if she were unmanageably in love with Tom and had just lost him. She wiped an eye with the back of a big fist. "What was I saying?" she added.

"Your kiddo."

"Oh, that one! Nice kiddo, my Buss."

"No. Tom."

"Oh. Them." She shrugged mightily. For a moment her stare went blank. Slowly her eyes began to well again, until I was fearful something had happened to Tom or Buss. But Aunt Dell had demolished them with her shrug. She had other roads to travel and was smiling in gentle, sad reminiscence. "Went to the nicest funeral over by Genesee. Day before yesterday."

"A relative? Someone close?"

"Nobody I'm acquainted with," she said matter-of-factly. "Just happened by the church. Stroke of luck, ainna? Poor man, died in his sleep. Only ninety." O, the Temporal! She sighed again, and then flung grief from her like a shawl and got back to business. "Grab me your vinegar jug, mister, and I'll show you how to mix you the brine, see? Toss me into the pot some salt."

Two-thirds of a measure of salt, nine measures of water, one-half measure of fragrant wine vinegar, repeated over and over. I memorized the proportions carefully as she filled the crock half full of cold brine. Then she tossed in, or caressed in, a mess of the stalks and heads of dill whose aroma filled the kitchen with all that is good on this earth.

But then I waited, in vain, for the revelation. From all her preparations and elation, I expected mystic rites next, or at least endless tasting with pursed lips. "Now all you do is throw in the beans?" The process seemed so simple for something she hinted was going to taste so marvelous.

"Self-evident," she answered, which is her elegant but happy way of saying "Yes" or "Sure."

She gave a grunt of vast smiling triumph and shoved a wooden lid over the crock.

"I'll bet they're going to be wonderful." I mustered all the bright expectation I could for what seemed to promise so little.

Aunt Dell, meanwhile, was gathering up her baskets and cigarettes and car keys and a few loose threads of conversation and several more little sighs of lost hope that she had left lying around the kitchen. She had been flushed, joyous, bubbling, openhanded, and jabbering all the while she was fussing over the beans and brine, but now unaccountably (for it had never happened before) she became a lady, taking her departure, and remembered restraint presumably was a virtue.

"They're rather good," she said in a small, deprecatory voice, sterile with refinement—I hope she never does it again, because she would make a deflated, useless lady.

Of them there are plenty anyway, but of Aunt Dell not enough.

*   *   *

By the next day, a strange and marvelous thing had already happened to the beans—spicy, sourish with dill and tinged with garlic, and coolly crisp. A day or two more and they were all the indispensable things Aunt Dell had hinted they would be. That is why a dill crock is as integral a part of summer as fireflies or sweet corn—you come in hot and parched from hoeing the garden or building a shed, and there is the crock like a big open fountain (you never seal the beans up in jars—that would be ungenerous) to dip into, and fish out one of the cool, crunchy, dilly vegetables. It is like the tub of pickles in old grocery stores. It is always there to plunge into elbow deep, a safeguard against life's inconstancies, a reminder that some good things will endure. It is like the miraculous pitcher, too. When it begins to look empty, you simply toss in more things.

For beans alone are not what give the crock its excitement. I had remembered Aunt Dell's explicit instructions: "Drop in what you want yet, mister. What comes out nobody knows." She meant that the joy of the crock was its openness to experiment. Green beans and wax beans went in, parboiled to get the fuzz taste off. But also, anything else, to be subtly metamorphosed by the earthiness of the dill. Raw small onions, raw very young carrots or strips of more aged carrots. Next I tried whole pods of sugar peas, before they were quite ripe, and these came out brittle, moist, and sweet. Then cauliflower florets. Grape leaves did no harm to the crock's mysterious ever-changing flavor, either. Nor did a sprig of cherry leaves.

"It's surprising," I said to Aunt Dell a week later, "the things you can dump into that pot and have come out wonderful."

Her face was sunny, her yellow-white hair glistened, her tall strong body moved amiably, but her blue eyes were clouded. She had come up to check on the dill crock (because, of course, she loved it like a deserted baby) and had rolled up her sleeve and poked a thick arm into the brine, all the way to the bottom, churning it around with walrus splashes until she came up with one of the sugar peas in its pod.

"Something fell in accidental?" she asked, in mild outrage.

I shook my head. She is a true, innate creator, and this was a vegetable she had never thought of flinging into the brine. She studied it like a piscatologist who had netted a new species. It seemed to depress her. She nibbled it critically. But even in her depression there was a certain joyousness.

"Rather good," she said at first, in her lady-voice. But there is strict justice in Aunt Dell's make-up, and soon her eyes lightened. "Never thought myself of dumping these things in."

And then she did it, flashing a bright smile with an upward jerk of her head. "Ainna?" she added.

And in another moment answered herself reflectively. "Self-evident!"

But something else was on her mind. She started out to her big limousine, which already was beginning to show signs of collapse though she had owned it only a month. Her eyes scanned the gardens, which, from luck and long, hard work, bloomed with a lustiness her garden had never known. The hill garden was pocketed with memorial roses, their hips ripening to glossy redness, verbena venosa and a dozen kinds of new daylily, from pink to a startling chartreuse. But she didn't see any of these. They bloomed in health. What Aunt Dell noticed was a pallid stalk of common wild fall aster that had seeded itself in a crack of the paving on the terrace. But its doom was plain. It was skimpy and starved. It couldn't last the summer. "Look the poor plant," she murmured.

Then her eyes moved up past the hills. "That nice Ed and Paulie Waldeen!" She looked toward their house, though it could not be seen. And this time her grief was real. Her big, joy-loving eyes were stinging, and where often her chin and mouth twitched in pity, now they were shaped stubborn as rock. Her love for Paulie and Ed was a cold reality.

She bent down suddenly and yanked the transient bloom from the crevice between the paving stones and flung it aside. Her broad face was purple, not with outrage, but with rebellion and refusal to accept whatever had so unfairly tainted the Waldeens' lives.

"Come down by our place when you want some more of them cukes or beans, mister. We got mushmelons too, by the galore," she said gruffly, and in one desolate, angry step climbed up what seemed like about six feet into her shiny car.

9

The Waukesha Mail-Pouch Robbery

COUNTRY men, I was surprised to learn, like to cook and like to talk about it and are not timid about admitting it. Every home around here has a dill crock, and as often as not it's the man who is its guardian. Down at the Corners along the bar of the Festive, Hank, who runs the slaughterhouse, Bud Devere, Clarence, who is a mechanic, and Joe, who sells reapers and binders, and Bob, who is our freight agent, will get to talking—on some nights they might talk baseball, or how to get new uniforms for the team, or fishing when the scent of quiet rain hangs on the evening air, or they might argue about which direction the Chesapeake & Ohio Railroad runs. I don't know why that's a favorite argument. It doesn't run within miles of here. No one yet has thought of looking it up on a map. But then again, on other nights, the talk as likely as not will turn on food.

Then Hank will tell the heretical way his mother didn't fry potato pancakes on top the stove, but baked them in the oven, studded with chunks of salt pork. Clarence mourns the van-

ished and forgotten flavor of real homemade blood sausage.
Bud tells about *fritto misto* in Italy or the *choucroute garnie* in
France—no one pays much attention to these dishes though,
because the lands they come from are too distant. Joe tells the
right way to hang and cook a wild duck. Bob answers with an
explosive description of lamb and cabbage cooked with caraway
seed and vinegar that he swears is goddam good. These are the
voices of men in love.

It is the same whisperings of love you hear in the Littens'
kitchen. When you go there and find noodles hanging over the
chairs to dry, and the breath of veal steak simmering in dozens
of slivered onions and sour cream floats on the air, and Carrie
and Millie are murmuring over their skillets and pots, you bless
the star that has led you to their door. Because wonderful things
are about to come to pass, and you are sure to be asked to stay
and partake of them. Supper leaves you as giddy as a balloon
ascension, reluctant to turn to earth afterward. You don't even
mind, later, when they lock the doors and windows, pull the
shades, switch on the radio, quiver visibly, and tune in "Dragnet." They love crime. Nothing quite stirred them so as the
Waukesha Mail-Pouch Robbery.

The robbery occurred late in summer and a week later the
robber was apprehended—it was a bold, admirable, and un-
complicated crime, a mail clerk simply helping himself to a
mail pouch with fifty thousand dollars cash in it. He was caught
a week later and given a stiff jail sentence.

For a week or so neighbors buzzed, locked doors at night that
had not been locked for years, bolted windows whose bolts were
too rusty to slide, and were generally enveloped in a mass fright
that all men feel in the darkness of the country when confronted by the unnatural. Normal things, like tornadoes or
whirlwinds, paralyzing drought, or a fifteen-foot drift of snow

piling up in a single night, or a month of rain until fungi grow between you and the chair, do not disturb country people; or a screech owl suddenly screaming its lovesick, banshee call in your eardrum, or a pair of wolves, strolled down from up north, found unexpectedly playing in your back yard, tails and red tongues flying, as Aunt Dell found them in her yard one winter morning.

These things are merely interesting. But a man not acting normal or usual scares you out of your wits. In the grocery store Harry and the customers talked with a haunted nervousness about what they would do with fifty thousand, even a little admiring envy in their voices, and at the Festive Country Club Hank and Bud Devere argued about where the mail pouch was hidden and where *they* would have hidden it. But they talked guardedly, not sure that the man next to them was not the one who *had* hidden it. (It was finally found under a bush in a public park right in Waukesha, a few blocks from the Post Office, with a thousand or so people walking past it every day. Or rather it wasn't just found there; the robber remorsefully told on himself and where it was hidden. No doubt his own country fear, of himself, of his daring, of his own skill in so irregular a thing as thieving, drove him to it.)

But once he was jailed the fear passed overnight. In true country fashion, people began to feel sorry for him. He was a nice boy, married, three children, maybe they needed clothing, etc., maybe his parents were old and ailing, etc., and maybe he was in a tough spot, perhaps with another woman, needed cash, etc., etc. A few of my neighbors even sent him gifts of candy or cookies and clothing and magazines in jail. Then that passed. He was forgotten.

By all, that is, save the Litten sisters, who until this day, I think, do not believe he was caught. They have a distrust of newspapers and policemen, though toward the latter they are a little more tolerant, believing that their inefficiency and bungling are only to be expected from anyone who would want to *be* a policeman. Hence, their scorn is tempered by the pity one feels toward harmless imbeciles. Anyway, radio cops are always catching criminals and spoiling the story.

They lived in a delicate fright and outrage for several months. It made them reluctant to stay home. They would call on a neighbor four, five, and six days in a row, making something like a formal, extended visit, flouncing home only to sleep —then move on to another neighbor, operating on the theory that one neighbor was as good as the next for their purposes but also no better, so they might as well keep calling on one until the welcome wore thin. Then they attacked the next house. In due time, mine.

I was glad to see them. It was over two months since the robber had been caught. Their Essex tootled up the hill as if it pursued the thief's getaway car and Shag, the old cocker, ran to hide, and Millie at the wheel spun the car around on a dime and clipped off a flowering crab, *Malus aldenhamiensis*, that I had nursed with buckets of water all summer, and Carrie in the back seat like a sovereign on a journey of state bowed stiffly, and got out and then opened the door for Millie. She forgot to wait until Millie came out and slammed the door shut again, but since Millie was getting out on the other side anyway, it didn't matter.

There had been a cold snap that week, the first frost, fires lighted, potted geraniums rushed inside. But after the first spell of dizziness, I was pleased to see Carrie and Millie, even if, because of the cold snap, they were wearing their mackinaws, earmuffs the size of muskmelons, and hunting caps. Millie was also wearing the natty pair of suède gloves I had sent them two weeks before for their birthday. Millie does not have a birthday, Carrie does not have a birthday, but "they" have "their" birthdays twice a year, one in May and one in September. Two presents apiece a year. Which doesn't make them dummies. But I noticed that over the suède gloves I had sent Millie she wore a pair of canvas mittens, frippery not impinging on practicality. For their birthday I had also sent Carrie a thin scarf, which she now took neatly folded out of her pocket, carefully unfolded it, wrapped it somewhat loosely around her mackinaw collar, and wore it the ten steps to the door, where she carefully took it off, folded it up again, and put it back in her pocket. I suppose it's still there.

"Came for a little canasta. Thought you might be lonely," Millie said cheerfully. "Being a bachelor and all. And living up here alone."

I didn't answer that, so far as I knew, they were unmarried too and living alone, or that I suspected this concern about my lonesomeness had come about only because they were scared stiff a robber might jump through their window, though that robber had been cooling his gumshoe heels in the Waupun Penitentiary for the past two months. Knowing how they dislike being disabused of their purely personal notions, I said nothing except to urge them inside.

I am always shy with them at the outset, as one is shy before rattlesnakes, but we soon settled down to playing cards in the big warm kitchen, where Carrie jumped up occasionally to poke the fire in the fireplace, scattering ashes effectively, or water the blooming plants on the windowsill, and once without a word Millie left and trotted out to the yard to bring in a log nearly as big as herself. These are capable women. She tossed the log into the fire with a merry bang.

And their capability does not lessen in a card game. They

play intently, if usually out of turn, or sometimes together, or sometimes one right after the other in quick, snatching succession, completely forgetting I am in the game (except to deal; they always slip the deal on to me somehow); and they can play and bid and ask questions and sneak glances through the window for the burglar and forecast the weather and tell each other a button is missing on your blouse, better sew a new one on, dear, did you lose it, well, look under your chair, all in one sentence or in one flip of the card.

Even so, the first half hour wasn't bad until after a fresh deal Carrie said, "Two no trump."

"This is canasta, not bridge," I hinted.

"Love it," Millie said. "Three no trump."

"Why don't we have some supper? Right now," I said, because Carrie was laying her six aces, four jacks, and three jokers down for a dummy. "I'll fix us a cocktail."

Millie threw down her cards. "The poor man's hungry. And we haven't got a single thing in the house except pork chops."

I don't know how they knew it, but Millie went directly to my icebox and brought out the pork chops I had bought that morning. Carrie was already tying on an apron. They shooed me out of the kitchen, but since I knew they would fix the chops in their special way, breaded, with a caper sauce, I left without reluctance and went to mix a martini. I know they drink sometimes, because I've had elderberry wine with them at their house, and when I took them their martinis they accepted them politely. But when I went to pour them a second I found them feeding their first to the geraniums, just like Victorian maidens did to the potted palms. Then they accepted the second drinks cordially. I left the kitchen again, feeling rakish.

Supper as always ended in a happy daze. They only nibble, passing the best morsels to each other's plate and sometimes forgetting and generously passing the same morsel back again, with little chipmunk-like, scampering sounds. But they love to see their guests eat, and sometimes give me their best morsels after they have been passed back and forth several times. Too, they scold if I don't wipe my plate clean with a crust of bread, a custom that fills one with expansive comfort and admiration.

After supper, they shooed me out again and did the dishes and stored them neatly away in the tool closet. Then we made another pot of coffee and sat around the kitchen table, for long moments not even speaking. Or sometimes for no reason Carrie would give a shy sweet young-girl laugh and then Millie would laugh, fairly hysterically, so I would laugh too, but no one ever said what we were so gay about. And because their fear of the night was so plain, I could do nothing but sit with them and drink a third pot of boiled coffee. Which wasn't coffee anyway. Millie forgot to put coffee in. So we had tea.

As they got ready to leave (which involved considerable bundling and unbundling, because again they kept putting on each other's wraps and then had long debates about whose was whose), Millie put out her hand.

"Well, come again," she said.

"Why, yes. Thank you. I will."

But plump Carrie looked thinner and thin Millie was a shadow, with having to return to their empty house, so I asked wouldn't they like to spend the night here with me. Millie and Carrie glanced at each other silently and then slowly retreated to their car. I think I actually hurt them.

I followed after them. It was a night with leaves racing up and down the black hills like a thousand brittle ghosts of cats chasing each other. But something else was wrong. Luckily it came to me in a flash. They were sitting in the car, but did not start the engine. Carrie had taken a hatpin from the glass flower vase in the car, where she keeps several, and poked it through her hunting cap, but they did not start off. In that flash, I guessed right. I was still a newcomer out here. To their other neighbors they could go four, five, or six nights in a row, but propriety and manners forbade their inflicting themselves on me; and the roster of their neighbors was nearly run through. Tomorrow, they would be home alone.

"Tomorrow night, I wonder would you let me drop over to your place for supper?"

Millie laughed. Miss Carrie sat up straight and smiled, and snapped her earmuffs on gingerly. The Essex chugged down the hill. Another night, one more night at least, of safety for them against rattling windows and prowling men.

*　　*　　*

That next evening they were all bold cheerfulness. Supper was a baked northern pike stuffed with celery and onions and fresh sage and, of all things, diced cucumber, and swimming in a fresh new lake of butter and *then* topped with buttered crumbs. Possibly as a return courtesy, they went into their parlor after supper to sit in their rockers, and left me to do the dishes, handing me the pair of rubber gloves they find indispensable for dishwashing. I washed, dried, even as a hint stacked the dishes in the cupboard where they belonged, and when I joined them in the parlor I found Miss Millie hunting under the sewing-machine hood where they keep their canasta decks. But remembering yesterday's game, I scouted in my mind for an escape. There were always the movies in the nearby towns. I hadn't opened my mouth though, to invite them, when Carrie smiled.

"That'd be lovely," she said.

Millie was already changing her shoes—from best to second

best. She says towns are dirty. "Hope they have Marie Dressler."

Carrie began filling a paper bag with popcorn from a large can (they take their own) and then they got into their old seal coats, not the mackinaws thankfully, and we started off in the Essex. They wouldn't drive in my car. They don't like convertibles.

"Too windy," Carrie said.

"But the top's up."

"Looks like one of your rear tires might blow," Millie murmured thoughtfully.

"These are new tires!"

"Look, Millie, what a narrow front seat. Did you ever?" Carrie asked with incredible disbelief.

"You always sit in the back anyway, Miss Carrie."

"Drafty in back," Carrie said.

"Wouldn't trust those tires. Don't like the looks of 'em," Millie said.

"Looks like your top might leak," Carrie said.

"It isn't raining," I said, but at last it came to me—they didn't want to hurt my feelings. My car was *unsuited* to them. They have an innate and dignified sense of their natural setting. Why else their gleaming barn-red house with white trim, not all white or cream or buff like other country houses, and the round nasturtium beds and inside the rockers and flowered rug and velvet-draped mantel? They didn't fit in a convertible. We climbed into the Essex with its window shades and glass vases and dignified height. Millie took the wheel with a lady-like clutch.

"Safer this way," she said flatly.

Safer it was. They live nine miles from Waukesha and in less than forty minutes we pulled up in front of the drugstore at the Five Points. Passing each neighbor's house on the way Millie had slowed down, sounding her horn, while Carrie waved from the back seat, though again it was a particularly black, starless, cat-chasing night. Waukesha, where the robber presumably still lurked, had been agreed upon only after a tussle. They suggested the movies in Nagawicka or Muckwonago. I said Waukesha, because the robber had been caught long ago, and that there was no danger. They said Pewaukee or Oconomowoc or Nemahbin. I said Waukesha. They said Okauchee or Chenequa. I said it sounded like an Indian conclave and fell silent, whereupon, surprisingly, Miss Millie steered toward Waukesha. They always concede with gracious stubbornness.

It wasn't until we started across the Five Points, a five-way intersection perilously busy with traffic, that I learned Millie and Carrie never cross the street together—or in the same direction. "In case of an accident," Carrie said. "We want to be sure one of us'll still be there to take care of the one that got hit."

And she started off alone at a clip. To circumvolve the Five

Points, however, necessitated crossing four streets and passing four stop lights, waiting at each one until the light was red in her unshakable belief that a red light means all motor traffic in all directions must stop. At each red light she half-closed her eyes, gazing trancelike (I completely shut mine), and started off at a brisk unswerving pace, through skidding cars and a blast of horns like New Year's Eve.

Millie and I had only one crossing to make, and I noticed she hung timidly on my elbow. But halfway across she stopped to watch Carrie, who was on her second stretch by now, having just made another red light. The cop on the corner began to chew on his whistle, not unreasonably, considering what we were doing to traffic, with Millie stock-still in the middle of one street and Carrie anteloping blindly across another. But as I coaxed Millie to the curb he only tipped his cap to her, blushed like a young girl, and tried to pretend he wasn't there. I knew him too, a likable young cop named Hilbert Dollwig, or "Dollie," and I thought, This is foolish, Hilbert, a gangling like you of two hundred pounds trying to play ostrich.

"Evening, Chief," Millie greeted him.

Dollie got a tic on the left side of his face, and I whispered to Millie that he wasn't the Chief of Police. Just an officer.

"Well, he ought to be. Nice boy, spite of being a copper. Found that stolen mail pouch yet, son?" she asked with a firm glare.

"Keep telling ya, Miss Litten," Dollie said, and sounded trapped, "we found that two months ago."

"Trying to cover up," Millie said, like a female Sam Spade. "I mailed a letter that day to a friend in Toledo. She never got it, did she? If you cops caught that robber and found the pouch, why didn't you mail my letter?" She looked remarkably rational and satisfied.

"I don't think there was any letters in that pouch, Miss Litten. Just the fifty thousand bucks." Dollie was growing red and sweaty, his tic was worse, and a peculiar silence was falling around us, a silence that gave one a sinking feeling, like life departing, until I realized it was only the blasting of horns dying down. And presently Carrie reached our side.

She was slightly winded, but the triumph of a channel swimmer lit her eyes. "Evening, Lieutenant. Disappointed in you boys. Where's our letter?"

"Excuse me," Dollie said.

"Can't excuse negligence," Millie said.

"Or cahoots," Carrie said.

"Well, begging your pardon," Dollie said. His tic was getting alarming and he looked at me helplessly. "There's a character over there across the street looks suspicious. Might be that pouch-stealer. Better tail him."

I felt sorry for him. Dollie is a polite and conscientious traffic cop and he shouldn't have been leaving his post. But he whizzed off, while the Littens looked at each other in a way to say things were finally getting done. And high time.

*   *   *

The movie turned out fine. They both slept through it, but Marie Dressler wasn't in the picture anyway. For fifteen or twenty years, I've been told, they've been watching for her in a new movie. They worship her and won't believe she's dead. Leaving the theater, Carrie opened her purse for a handkerchief and crumpled among the hairnets, horseshoe nails, and dominoes she carries there, I saw a grimy envelope. It was addressed to someone in Toledo.

"Miss Carrie," I said, "there's an envelope in your bag—"

Carrie glanced at it. "Must be a letter we wrote." And when I offered to mail it for them, she snapped, "Certainly not. Have it stolen from the mail pouch again?"

"That *is* the letter," I said.

But we were back at the corner (which for the first time in years was copless) and Carrie had already begun her return tour around the Five Points. The corners were dark and deserted now, the arc light swinging, wind banging against the IGA store and the five-and-ten, and the maples along the street shaking dark fingers to chase away the shadows but only spilling out more, and as she waited for the red light Miss Carrie looked solitary and very small. The green light glowed on her pale tired face that all at once looked expressionless, half dreamlike, half lost, as she stood waiting. Then the red light flashed, adding warmth, adding life, and I was glad.

"Sometimes I think we might as well cross the streets together, though," Millie was saying at my side. I had not spoken. Her words careened along the windy night. And she too looked frailer, unattached. She looked cold, despite the bundling sealskin coat. She was watching Carrie's lonely, silent progress and I thought I heard sadness and the broken sigh of time's passage in her voice. "Can't see how one of us girls would be much good without the other."

I can't, either.

10

The First Leaf

I HAD watched uneasily while the first leaf fell. I had seen it as early as the beginning of August. It was a pin oak, not very withered, still a glossy green, but it marked a warning as it fell. There was the sudden gloom of knowing all things must end—even this newfound peace and fullness could end. And would winter again be as despairing and paralyzing as the first winter had been?

But then from a neighboring field that had once been my grandfather's field, I heard the distant racket of Vic Eckstein's tractor, the hum of its engine in the sunny still day, the sound of harvest, and the unexpected but blessed assurance that the seed of the grain harvest meant next year's life. The winter must pass. . . .

I looked at the tree from which the first leaf had fallen in the August silence and knew that the creeping dormancy of the trees, making the leaves fall, was only an interval in its continuity. Affirmation, rather than decline. Perpetual renewal. Life, not death. Unaccountably, I thought of Paulie Waldeen.

Walking with Tom in the woods I'd discovered a formula for Reducing Man to His Own Size, or How to Knock Some of the Bigheadedness out of Him. It was the business of the seed again. The tractor-sound of affirmation was still in my ears when Tom said he'd rather be a tree surgeon than a farmer (his need to take care of things!). I wanted to say, That's all right, Tom, but you needn't think these trees need you. I was feeling resentment, perhaps, because at last, in spite of all my reasoning against it, I would in a few days be returning to New York City.

My fears had mockingly reversed themselves. Now the thought of New York made my nights sleepless, my head and nerves pound. But irrevocably this time, my bags were packed; letters written; a ticket bought. For the very reason that once I could not go back, now I must go back—because I had no money. During the first winter of stunning despair, looking across the white hills toward what had once been my grandfather's farm, I had begun to write down all I could remember or had heard about him—perhaps in angry answer to the dreams I had when I first left Wisconsin a decade before, only to find that in New York the moment to write a story could never be squeezed in among the hours required to make a living, to make a noise, to keep one's footing. But in the country there were far too many accusing hours to fill. Some of these stories sold. They looked fine in print. One bought a badly needed new suit to return to New York in now. One paid Dr. Beemiller's bill. The check in payment of another, with the affection one feels toward all small things, I saved as a curio.

Too, as I remembered my grandfather, I remembered his son, my father, who had run away from these hills as a young man to become a big city gambler. I began to remember many things about my father and mother together, stories they told me, stories I myself had watched unfold, how they met, loved, fought for each other, bore a son, grew rich, grew poor again, stood faithful to each other; and how always that mother and son were the staff of life to the father, but the whisper of dice, the riffle of cards, the hushed click-clack of chips, were its blood. That story, as I had hinted to Bud Devere, I wrote during the second spring and summer. Perhaps unknowingly I began that novel as long ago as the previous autumn, when one of Ernie Pollock's wires had wisecracked cheerfully, as he was cutting me out of a job and livelihood: *Why don't you write a book?* I know I saw that wire often on the pages as I typed away. I wrote with fury for Ernie and love for my parents, with rage toward life and hope for tomorrow.

A month ago, that book had quietly been published. Its success was critical, not financial. So now there could be no more waiting to return to New York. There was a job to find, new clients and accounts, the work, the rushing, the need to make noise and be heard and to find sudden success again.

Tom and I walked slowly. I tried not to let him know what I was thinking. That fear, grown swollen in the past year, was a large part of my not wanting to return. That I had, ironically, grown used to small places. That youth can start out in big cities with empty pockets, but for an older man . . . ?

Around us the woods, hills, kettles, lay in such self-enclosed silence as if they were another country, superiorly governing themselves, and glancing indifferently sometimes toward their neighboring nation of human beings which, when they felt like it, they would devour. I was thinking of myself not walking through these woods but racing through a hot and airless subway. Listen, Tom, it doesn't matter to the woods and hills whether you or I or anyone else walks here or not. They have no need of us. They don't know grief. You might say a man has his own glory because he can think and feel and the trees cannot. But also a man knows he must die, but the tree doesn't, which does not make man the lucky one. Virginia Woolf may have heard death occur in the forest, when she saw a tree crash down. But no grief was set loose by that death. Only absence, the crowded trees swinging out their branches to fill the space where the tree had been.

Of course. A jewelweed, or touch-me-not, or snapweed, which will scare you to death by its habit, when scarcely touched, of exploding its seed pod, had just burst open as Tom brushed against it, flinging its dry, black seeds right and left in a miniature bombardment. In the quiet, self-sufficient woods, a dropping seed is a greater wonder than the footfall of any human. The woods lives by itself, loving wind and rain and sun and the animals and insects it harbors. It has an impervious beauty, existing only for its own pleasure and is a chaos of survival, the ropelike vines reaching out to strangle the trees while the trees grow stout to burst the vines apart.

"Tom—!" I cried suddenly, and repeated what Paulie had whispered to him in the Dog Hollow. That D. H. Lawrence had never seen a wild thing sorry for itself.

*   *   *

Only, it sounded different and angry now. Because I had to leave. Because I was missing the land already.

And because, a day earlier, I had already said good-by to Paulie Waldeen. She wasn't sorry for herself, whatever there was to be sorry for. Like other neighbors, the Waldeens felt proprietary toward the woods because both had played there when they were kids, sledding in winter and picking trilliums in spring and courting in summer, which gradually made me come to accept them as the true inheritors of this earth. Since

her first day of trespassing in the Dog Hollow, I'd often find
Paulie walking in the woods, alone sometimes but usually with
Ed, their new inhuman aloofness in tune with the new aloofness of the trees. That November day, of the autumn when I
was leaving, they were on Juniper Hill.

They had already become people I didn't know. Ed was
building a fire. He was sportily dressed in a loose maroon cor-
duroy jacket, a silk kerchief, bright socks. He was someone you
might have met at a hunt meet or horse show, rather than a
farmer picnicking alone with his wife on a hill. But that was
another new thing about the Waldeens: they seemed to have
gone into a perennial courtship, like Ed dressing up for Paulie.
It was cold. The fire was good. But the Waldeens didn't seem
to enjoy my coming upon them. The trees had already lost most
of their leaves and another hillside nearby was covered with
migrating white and gray birds that from a distance looked
eyeless and tragic. Around their fire, though, Ed and Paulie
looked comfortable and complete.

Paulie was opening a bottle of wine, and with her babushka
and the slanting sun behind her she somehow got the look of
a Breughel painting—the plenitude and blessedness of the
land. She laughed, high and clear, when a little of the wine
spilled on her hand—it sounded gay and busy, the way she had
sounded at her party. But I saw her face. It was a doll's face
grown old. It had forgotten to stay a doll's, and was feeling terrible human emotions. Everything flexible in its pattern had
gone wild and uncontrolled. There was a sudden haste in it.
The small face, so open to emotion, was a racing field of it,
every thought or flicker of feeling leaving brutal miniature hoof-
prints on it. But hope was there. The round intelligent eyes,
two crests or badges of her spirit, fought to struggle out of a trap
with the most useless and wonderful defiance I had yet seen.

Even so, a civility and gaiety broke through. I didn't know that they already knew I was leaving soon—perhaps that was why they could afford to open up. I would soon be gone. We drank the wine, and Ed with his raw grin talked about the big profit he had made on his steers that fall, which he enjoyed, and soon Paulie curled up in Ed's long arm and actually went fast asleep. Ed hardly seemed to notice her. He went on talking and drinking. But you could tell his arm was around her like a band of iron. They began to look like part of the earth, part of the hilltop, of the surrounding land, plain farm people in love. Paulie's sleeping face was out of shape against Ed's chest, but it was clear and peaceful as a wildflower. They began to look as if they would be there that way forever, and I wish now that they were.

When Paulie woke up, after ten or fifteen minutes, a somber watchfulness had come over her. She looked startled and dismayed that she had wasted time. Curled against Ed, she was only half his size, but now she had become his guardian. Without looking up at him, she fell to untying one of his shoelaces and retying it more neatly, in the absent but yet intense way a mother will repair a child's dishevelment. Her hands were like moths fluttering around his big foot.

"I'm leaving to go back to New York in a few days," I said. Because, suddenly, I was in their way.

"Oh?" Paulie said.

"Lucky guy," Ed said, and did not look away from the fire.

I had inexplicably bumped against their big sign. The feeling of hurry came from everywhere, from birds overhead, from a gust of wind. Something else was clear, too. They wanted to be back in each other's arms, on the hilltop. Sorry, we like you and this is your hill, but couldn't you please go away now?

The news of my leaving was as if I hadn't said it. Yet it

changed everything. It was of course their own separation they
were thinking of. Ed shoved himself forward and raked the
fire into coals. Beneath the handsome tan was a gray fear. He
coughed into the smoke, but it was more than a cough—it was
something shaking itself out of his body.

"So you're going back to New York," he said after a while.
Both were looking at me politely. Go away, won't you? "Lucky
stiff."

"Ed, watch out. You're in the fire!" Paulie said. She pulled
at his jacket.

"I'm O.K.," he grinned at her.

"*Please* take care of yourself," she commanded brusquely.
"That coat isn't warm enough, anyway. You should have worn
a leather jacket. And you're sitting on the damp ground."

"I'm O.K.," Ed said again. He sat back on his haunches and
coughed again, but in a moment the paroxysm subsided. He
wet his lips as if they thirsted desperately for water.

It was Paulie taking care of him—Ed, who was strapping, and
had a body strong and powerful as one of his own farm animals.
Now he sat cowed, smiling feebly, a child with hunched shoulders and trusting eyes trying to find something to trust. And
Paulie comforted him: she hung near him like a nurse, fending
off whatever strange thing was coming nearer and nearer to
harm him.

Unexpectedly she jumped to her feet and was running like
a small laughing girl at play to the edge of the hill. There were
dark patches down below, and the blue dusty-grape color along
the horizon, and a kind of emerald sky above that and then
below it the round hills, bleak perhaps in autumn, but biscuit-
colored and henna and rust.

"It's wonderful, isn't it?" Paulie marveled. But her enjoyment was as actual as it was surprising, and she had mastered

something, her small, thin body stretching on tiptoe from the hilltop. "I can never get enough of this hill. You're lucky to own it. I'll bet you never slept up here. Ed and I have, often. Before you bought the place. Doesn't it make you feel grateful?"

Affirmation, I thought. Life was yanking at her, the muscles under her warm skin grabbing back at it; her body flicked like a pony's. She saw Ed opening their lunch hamper. She could not see Ed's eyes, wet like a baby's. He shook all over without any sound but yet he steadied his hand enough to lift bottles and dishes from the hamper.

"Ed, I can do that. You just sit." There was a piping frenzy in her flute-voice too, then. "*Please*, Ed, you go sit on the rock over there and rest. Why don't you get out of the smoke? It makes you cough so." The last, I knew, was the most obvious lie she had ever told—he wasn't coughing from smoke. She looked up at me baldly. Her eyes were steady and smiling and bold, and didn't see me at all. "I'm sorry we can't ask you to eat with us. There isn't enough," she said politely and shamelessly.

"I couldn't stay anyway."

"That's too bad." Go away.

"No, it isn't," I said. It's my hill.

Paulie put out her fragile hand. "I hope New York is wonderful. Ed, wouldn't you love New York? Don't you wish we were going?"

Later I learned they did go there for several weeks, but never looked me up. Standing now on the dusky hill, she was perfectly controlled. Gentry, I thought. The true blood of the earth. Knows how to lie when she feels like it and doesn't ask anyone's permission. But can do it graciously. The finest lady in the land. She even looks regal. Slight, imperious, iron-willed, undefeated.

"While you're going to shows and things, we'll just be sitting here," she said suddenly. And smiled with a kind of aching friendliness. "We'll hold the fort while you're gone."

Yes, in your dark bolted house.

"We'll go some day. We'll look you up," Ed said. He was able to look at me directly now, and was grinning again.

"Thanks for the hill," Paulie said. "Oh, Ed, look at you— you've got a big hole in your heel."

I didn't wait to see whether she got out yarn and a darning needle right then and there to fix it for Ed, but it was the impression she gave—except, that is, for the other impression that still lingered in both of them, of eagerness to be in each other's arms. I remember feeling a sharp envy of the married state, of the united front that was able to kick me off my own hill. It is the loneliest feeling there is, when two out of three people want to make love. But it was not so much physical, as an abstract fight against time.

And there was at least this much I knew now, that their separation was coming, perhaps through some disease (it was) in Ed or in Paulie (it was). But the song of life that sang so clearly in Paulie that day on the hill made me blindly and stupidly certain, as I made my way home through the woods and left them there alone, as they wanted, that whatever it was that had happened to them, it was Ed it had happened to; he was the one who was stricken or diseased or caught short or wiped out. Though in any separation, I thought, which needs courage most, the one leaving or left?

*   *   *

I went to New York, found a job in another agency, at half the salary I had earned before, and with three men sharing my office, when once I had gloried in my own. But in February, by luck, I was able to come back home. Being in the city had been on time borrowed from my new, adopted country. Once I had loved cities but suddenly didn't. The Verdi Square women were still there, looking colder now, walking aimlessly along the street, shopping for a single pork chop or a half pint of whisky, going back to their no less cold or barren rooms.

That winter I walked the streets of my old neighborhood with the feeling I had never been there before, so little are you remembered and so quickly do new curtains hang in your window. I kept wishing I were walking along the snow-drifted lane through Grandma Mill's place, taking the short cut to our village Post Office. The high buildings weren't quite so beautiful. I had learned to look at high trees. Even the food in restaurants didn't taste as good as I remembered, because they didn't have Millie and Carrie or Aunt Dell for chefs. Everyone, at the crowded tables, looked alone.

I went to parties, but no one seemed to know anyone else very well, or, more importantly, wanted to, and no Walter Cwyms brought out carefully hoarded homemade applejack, and no neighbors came bringing homemade bread or crust-baked hams. I couldn't sleep nights because of the noise. I couldn't work days because of the noise. There was no air, space, time. Children did not sled down hills or race through fields; they played listlessly and sheepishly on the narrow sidewalks of Central Park. I was one of the assistant engineers who liked to watch steam shovels dig huge excavations along Fifth Avenue or Madison and see the intricate metal framework go up. But this no longer seemed so marvelous as beavers building their intricate dams.

I began again the old New York habit of worrying about how to do two irreconcilable things at once, how to get by, how to slow down. How to see things on the way, as Bud Devere had been smart enough to do it. There was enough talk, all right, the world awareness I was afraid I was losing in the country. But only the old talk about destruction and the power to prevent it—power in terms of money and guns, never of the power to capture and lift men's minds and spirits. Next question, please? But never any answer. Never love of life. Only fear of death. Never gratitude. Only despair.

Was this the city I had loved so blindly? I suddenly remembered two things—the gratitude my mother had said I would find, when she came down Juniper Hill with the tin pailful of raspberries. The gratitude that was Paulie's, standing on tiptoe on Juniper Hill, loving the sky, wind, earth. I thought I heard their voices saying something so ludicrously simple that I should have heard it long ago: *You're supposed to like being alive!*

In the country there had been no bounds, as when the wild fox had raced so easily and joyously to save his freedom. And then, easily, joyously, came the chance to save mine.

On that gloomy autumn day, when leaves were falling, along with all my hopes and my life, and the wires from Ernie Pollock had arrived, and Dr. Beemiller had just told me I must not leave the country—surely then the seed was planted. Today, unknown to us, provides for tomorrow. I had already learned it to the distant whirr of Vic Eckstein's tractor: that tomorrow's birth is in the death of the harvest. For now, while I was back in New York, I was told that the novel I had written, out of all those things I had recalled about my father and mother together, was to become a motion picture.

It was as easy, as joyous, as that.

And it meant, moreover, the final mockery of all. But a gentle, loving mockery, which is a way life likes to joke with us too. Because now there was all the money I would need, for a long

while to come. The past years were obliterated—at least, all
that could ever be obliterated. I could, if I chose, live out my
days in New York. I need never stifle in small towns among
small people again. I need not suffer again in bitterness or
freezing regret or burning anger. No more Millies or Carries,
Buds, Aunt Dells, Fifes, Toms, woods, snowy hills, grapes in
bloom.

I was walking down Madison Avenue. I swerved over toward
the New Weston bar. It was only when the men inside kept
looking at me that I knew I had tears in my eyes. But this was
a mist of happiness. I took the next train home.

*   *   *

And I knew I would never have to leave the Welsh Hills
again, unless I wanted to. But it bothered me, with the remote,
passive affection one feels toward an old love, that I left New
York with such relief. I was growing old, or disgruntled, or
sour.

But soon after I came back to the country in February, in a
bitterly cold twilight, that great rural tragedy took place—a
barn fire. It took only half an hour for the fire to destroy what
had taken an entire spring and summer, and thousands of man-
hours, and intelligence, and prayers against inclement weather,
and prayers against treacherous beetles or borers, to produce.
The barn, with everything stored in it, harvest and machinery,
along with the farmer's hope for a winter's reward of rest and
security, burned to the ground in a great shock of light, and as
swiftly as any human hope can die. Against that flaming light
the farmer stood silhouetted, watching himself fall in ruins and
ashes.

But while the fire was burning, well over half a hundred men
appeared from nowhere, three-quarters of whom the stricken

farmer had never seen in the neighborhood before. These men fought the fire, singeing their own hair and clothing and bodies to rescue the cattle, and when their effort to save the barn itself proved useless, as it always is, and the barn was gone, stayed on to spend the rest of the evening driving the farmer's frantic cattle a mile away to safety and shelter and warmth. And then helped the farmer milk the cows and finish his evening chores, a job which lasted until two o'clock in the morning. One of the men who helped was dressed in an expensive overcoat and wore fine, hand-stitched gloves. He had been driving by in a Buick Roadmaster when he saw the fire, but stayed to join with a not-well-hidden excitement and exuberance in the milking, something it was plain at first he had not done in years. But his hands soon remembered, and it grew clear that this rich man's roots were the same as the roots of those around him in overalls and leather jackets, and that he seemed relieved and happy to have found them again.

It was not until halfway through the night that these exhausted, freezing men, who without a second's deliberation had just enacted the best possible definition of the word "neighbor," started home to begin their own chores. Not even knowing, the rich man among them, that they had all been friends.

"This kind of thing never happens in cities," the stranger said, grinning at the other men, all of whom only glanced at him blankly as if to ask "Why not?" He got into his big car and drove off, alone.

Someday, I might have been that man. I knew then without doubt that this was the world I wanted to live in forever. Some of us went into the glum, defeated farmer's house to wash up and have a beer, or the coffee and sandwiches the women had been making, and already neighbors were talking about a new barn and what machinery or tools they'd be able to lend him in spring. You could still see the smoking ruins through the dark window. But already they were less black and desolate.

I looked at the men around me and knew that a journey home was complete.

11

Brief Stay

IT WAS still a sad journey, nevertheless, because it meant leaving behind in the city many things I had grown to love, the stimuli of galleries and concerts, the impact of so many people from all over the world, the flavor of the taverns haunted by old seamen down near the Battery, the sense of vanished history when the first snow falls along Bleecker Street in the Village, the muted color of the river in winter twilights, the rushing roar of the tunnels, the aerial humming of the high bridges. Especially it meant leaving friends behind—such as Anna, the one who had learned to dance at Sibelius' house.

Hers was a city story, and explained as well as any the loneliness, and especially the peculiar indifference, of American cities. She belonged in cities, but the kind she knew and loved were the old slow-moving ones, rich in memories and customs, warm and friendly, all dead now since the war or out of her reach. But she would not leave New York, as I had. She clung to it to the last gasp. Cities were in her blood, but the old kind that had nourished it were gone, and the new kind were its poison. She was a free soul, which the modern impersonal city does not like. She had visited out here the past summer. She seemed to find peace—but she could not stay. *Though I love them, I do not understand them, your trees and meadows!* She said it ruefully, but also gaily. Strangely, though she came of an old people and they were the new, the Waldeens and Aunt Dell and Bud Devere could listen to her story and understand it better than others, perhaps because they were free souls, too.

She had been born in Finland, where her father was an emissary of Finland's freedom to the Tsar's court—which was splendid training to make her the furious Russian-hater, White or Red, she became. After one visit to St. Petersburg, her father was kept imprisoned an entire day and evening in a coach by two drunken, arrogant, insolent coachmen, the Tsar's own, capriciously held incommunicado by them and all the while not knowing whether he was on his way to Siberia or back home to his family in Helsinki.

In Helsinki, just before the first war, as a girl in her early teens, wearing a white ruffled dress, she had learned to waltz in Sibelius' house, with Sibelius improvising waltzes at the piano, after he had dismissed the string orchestra hired for the party because he could not listen to its insipid music. But waking up one morning during the 1917 revolution, she found most of her relatives dead, as well as half her friends of her own age, the young men and girls she had studied and danced and driven with through the parks. It must have been heartbreaking to leave Finland with its swamps and clean old somberly-lighted cities, and wet cliffs, and waterfalls, and fur-clad winters and quiet supper parties. On New Year's Eve the servants used to bring ladles of molten lead into the drawing room for the children to drop into a bucket of ice water, reading their futures in the swiftly solidifying shapes. Hers must have formed into tormented shapes.

Her family sent her, then only fifteen, to the United States, where she began the long, painful, homeless, confused, bitter journey of exile through New York to inland cities, back briefly to Buda Pesth and Pontresina and Ragusa (these were her rightful haunts) and back to the inland cities, through marriage and divorce and financial insecurity and more insecurity and finally back to New York, her starting place, and the last aching days. But her story has a grandeur about it.

"Why in hell didn't she find some small town and settle down in it?" Bud Devere would ask. "Like you're doing?"

"She couldn't."

She really couldn't. There are those for whom the country will not answer. She was committed to cities.

Bud finally agreed. "But she was such a gay babe. And she had looks. Nice shape. Good dresser, like the French women. And I guess you'd say she was a lady."

She was proud, small, boyishly thin, looking younger than she was, and always laughing. Her gaiety was the kind that, surprisingly, had no loneliness in it at all. It made any meeting with her a light, effulgent, winy experience. For she talked with a blessed tongue and could not endure anything dull— any infinitesimal event, any phrase of music she had heard, or paragraph she had read in magazine or book, was enough for an hour's rollicking conversation, punctuated often by the youthful, rippling laugh she never lost. But as well as she could talk, she could listen. She never missed a point or nuance, listening as whole forests are said to listen in the still night for sounds of fire, flood, or dangerous wind.

With her remarkable accent which she never lost (and about which Aunt Dell said admiringly, "She talks funny, ainna? Not American! It's rather good—") was coupled a fluid and imaginative English vocabulary. She thrilled over the subtleties of words, the way a Frenchman feels them, but her American slang was disastrous.

To learn the time, didn't one ask genteelly, "And what then does your turnip say?" Or her "dump"—it meant any abode she had. She used the word with a curious, affectionate respect. Her "dump," wherever it was, had become her whole world. It had shrunk that small, and in it she wanted to live alone. But her small world was a gay one. She would invite you into it with a gentle, murmuring enthusiasm, perhaps at nine in the evening ("But for the love of God, why would you have eaten dinner already?"), explaining that she had this small beast roasting in her oven, and of course you must share it with her. Suddenly, somehow, life had become jocose for Anna—perhaps for no other reason than that she had seen a burst of spring flowers in a florist's window, or in some shop had come across a pair of gloves of glacé kid, a certain kind her mother had bought her one time during a childhood visit to Prague. At times like this, life with her was lyrical, carefree, and offering hardly any problems at all, certainly none that were insurmountable. That the "small beast" roasting in her oven was a goose, and that geese take at least three or four hours to roast, was neither a surprise nor a concern. She liked having dinner at midnight or one in the morning. So did the one or two guests lucky enough to sit down to it with her, after an outstanding number of cocktails, after hours of even more astounding, laughing talk. Life was a grand festivity behind her doors.

You drank long rows of martinis with her, or daiquiris in summer, or bourbon. But she is the only person I have known who, though she drank devoutly, never had any guilt about it. It is affecting to know that her last job should have been as nurse in a private, swank New York "home for dopes and drunks." She had learned nursing during the revolution in Finland, as many of her class did, and repeatedly she returned to it as other jobs failed. Night shift, too, which meant that her private cocktail hour subsequently began at seven in the morning, an hour that, if not to her, was at least a little erratic to the few friends she would sometimes ask to join her.

But never any guilt touched her, even when she began setting her bed on fire. Rather, a kind of amazement that liquor should do this to one—she was hurt by it, as if a friend had turned on her. Though also, despite the amount she might consume in the interstices when it made life tolerable for her, she never became a drunkard. It was indispensable, but still at her command. She was unacquainted with the hangover. Awakening always found her bright. Her life irrevocably, that much she knew in her quick wisdom, must be hers to live and only hers. So, beholden to no one, how could she feel guilt? She was isolated from a world which did not want her anyway. But she insisted on remaining her own definition of a human being in that world.

*   *   *

And then she bought the battleship. There was nothing unreasonable to Anna in the idea of buying a battleship—she held the proud, invincible, if ornate, view of life. It was after the war. She had come from an inland city to live in New York again during the war, for one more cheerful stab at life, and with a bold hope to make life at last behave reasonably toward her. But in three or four years she had not yet been able to find a habitable place to live; then, and until her death, she shared a Swedish friend's two-room, four-flight walk-up.

All she had come to want was a small place of her own, a few clean rooms, space for her books (Colette, G. B. Stern, endless Finnish and Swedish volumes) and beloved piano, an old Bechstein that had traveled everywhere with her, and her stupendous collection of tattered, disarranged sheet music. For a series of summers, long ago, she had returned to Vienna and Paris to study the piano. The music, piano, books, were stored in my apartment while I still lived there, the one near Verdi Square, against the day when she would again find the place of her own which she always sought but never found. When I left, the books, the piano, the ragged sheet music, had to be put into storage. She chatted casually while the van pulled away, as though nothing at all important were happening. She might have made an excellent pianist, though for many years she never played except on evenings when I would be out and the apartment was empty, and she could come alone, walking through the wind across Verdi Square, high heels clattering, always racing, until she could lock herself in the apartment and sort through her boxes of torn velvety-with-dust sheet music, faded as if it had been stored away at least a hundred years. It was illuminating music, little-known pieces. A Bach (Wilhelm Friedemann) organ concerto. Unheard Mendelssohn songs. Unknown Scandinavian composers. The lesser-played Chopin mazurkas. Some waltzes by Sibelius.

She had a few thousand dollars saved up in the bank—her backlog—which she was always planning to invest in preposterous schemes to coup a million, such as a housing project of collapsible houses, or magazines dedicated to beauty parlor operators (for which she would be permitted to review books in its pages in return for her investment!), or factories to manufacture three-wheeled motor cars, or expeditions to Zanzibar to look for something or other, projects from which she had to be restrained by friends until finally she did plunge, and that caused her end. Now, however, she was determined to use some of that money. She could not exist any longer without a "dump" of her own. In *The Times* she read that the United States was disposing of some submarine chasers it no longer needed for less than a song.

Why shouldn't she have one to live in? She envisioned attractive curtains on the portholes. River life would be peaceful and, God! she longed for peace. A place for her music, piano, books. But how would she reach her battlecraft, anchored out in the East River? Why, she could have a dinghy, and the picture of herself toddling into her dinghy and rowing herself home over the black water among tooting barges and moaning tugs was not one that seemed at all unlikely to her.

She told about it herself, indignant at its outcome. Down to the Battery she had gone, to interview the proper naval authority, and him at least she found to be a gentleman as well as an officer while she explained her intentions to him. He listened courteously and sympathetically, though a sailor on duty in the office broke into such gagged guffaws at her proposal that the officer had to bang his desk, crying, "I must demand that you stop this demonstration at once, sailor!" Anna thought this considerate of the gentleman officer. Her withering glare toward the sailor I can supply myself.

"Madame," the officer said, "have you thought of the expense involved in heating and lighting such a vessel as this?"

"But do they not then have little dynamos to overcome such difficulties?"

Silence from the captain. A purple choke from the sailor. Next, from the nice captain, "I sympathize with your wishes, Madame." Anna, telling it, managed to make the officer sound exactly like the captain of *H.M.S. Pinafore*. "But before making your purchase, might I suggest you enquire as to the rental of dock facilities at which to anchor your vessel?"

"But I would not be permitted, then, to anchor my scow right in the river, which, God knows, is big enough?"

"Indeed not, Madame. A dock is essential by regulation. Port of New York Authority."

This was the felling blow. The worthy officer supplied Anna with a list of companies that owned docks, and dutifully she made the rounds of them, looking for a place to drop anchor. Just a small space, she asked for.

But could poor Anna ever find a corner of her own to live in? "Do you know," she said, trembling in indignation, "and I do not lie, but the cheapest rental I could find was five thousand dollars a day?"

But at least the captain had been nice to her. She did not overlook that.

*   *   *

She came out to visit in the country only once, but in that short summer visit a new Anna walked the fields. She might, at moments, have been back in Finland or in her youth. Lumbering, moo-eyed cows enthralled her. She talked much about Lapland, her family's summer home. The northern lights made her stand straight and silent. She laughed and drank and made life golden, and visited around among my new friends, the Waldeens or Aunt Dell, helping with baking or making salads, fighting off the shyness they felt at first toward her, and gradually becoming their friend, when she almost never made friends any more. And she would be up sunning herself by seven in the morning, already having washed out her blouses and full cotton skirts, hung merrily over fences and bushes, and she made a hit with Stag, the bartender over in Genesee, and

discovered pinball machines, and by five in the afternoon would
be sitting on the terrace, fresh, immaculate, prettily gowned,
waiting for cocktails again and the long hours of chuckling talk
that would follow. I suggested she choose an acre of land, one
of the hills perhaps, and using her bank balance, build herself
a small house against what she liked to call the twilight of her
days. Then for hours each afternoon she would climb the hills,
searching for a site with a suitable view.

But she never came back to claim her acre—she never really
wanted one. She was a city woman, even if she was trapped
there. One job in New York grew more despairing, more throt-
tling, less remunerative, than the last. She had tried peddling a
children's encyclopedia from door to door when she hated sales-
men who rang her own doorbell; clerking in a department
store; selling travel books for a small publisher who turned out
to be nonexistent; nursing in a charity hospital for Negroes,
where she was curiously happy; next in a fantastically expensive
plastic surgeon's private hospital; next in the swank place for
dopes and drunks. What happened to her in New York? Why
did stone-faced New York dislike her so? Her aloofness, arro-
gance, demand for quality? In a way she and New York remained so compatible. But that compatibility was only in con-
cert halls, theaters, parks, along the river, galleries, restaurants
—never when the city's people were personally involved. Her
life was a long argument with shopkeepers, subway guards,
and policemen, from whom she would try to ask directions that
never seemed to lead her anywhere.

As it grew increasingly difficult to earn a living, she began to
live on her bank balance. She never really wanted to leave New
York—except for such unlikely places as Caracas, in Venezuela,
which she could not afford. (She did during her last winter
take an end-of-the-season excursion to Florida by bus, all ex-

penses paid, including one cocktail served at a "tour party" in the hotel lobby!) A return to Europe was unthinkable. Never once had she considered returning to Helsinki and its dark shadows, still darker now since her last surviving brother had been killed by the Russians in 1940.

Still, she had no home. New York certainly cared little. The dreary, four-flight walk-up. She discussed new wild schemes for earning a livelihood—she could fling herself against the flimsy bannister of her walk-up, suffer a few fractures, and sue the landlord for a fortune. It was hard to convince her it might not work.

I remember what she said the last time I saw her. It was in February, just before I left New York to come back home permanently to the Welsh Hills. "Heavenly God, the magnificent expectations with which I came to New York, it seems such a few years ago!" She looked frightened and pale, but then she was laughing again.

Then, as others far wiser have done before her, she acquired the peculiar, tragic compulsion to believe in fortunetellers and spiritualists. She clutched for her last directives from them. Another newspaper advertisement this time offered a woman's shoeshop for sale. The perfect small business for her, where she would be her own boss in her own world! On Broadway. It did not seem senseless to her that this shop was three flights up in a grimy, disreputable-looking building. Friends tried to reason with her. But the spiritualist she consulted for one dollar buoyantly said Opportunity, though grime-laden, was waiting for her, pregnant with reward.

All her money went into the shop. The stock turned out to consist entirely of sandals, and these only in size AAAA. She sat several days in her shop, dusted, rearranged the sandals, I suppose, perhaps tried some on, read avidly while waiting for

customers though none ever showed up, went home the third night, had cocktails, and, like a Scandinavian cousin of hers who refused to be tangled in tawdry circumstances, like Hedda, shot herself in the breast.

Would it have happened had she claimed her acre, stopped racing across Verdi Square, or, as Bud suggested, found a small city or town and settled there? I don't know. I wish she had tried it. But she couldn't. It was spring when the telegram came. Bud Devere happened to be up here, helping repair a faulty rainpipe.

He looked toward the fence where the white lilacs had opened. "She picked the right time."

"What do you mean?"

Then he said that she had told him, during her summer visit out here when they were sitting under the shade of the lilac bushes having a drink, that she was glad she had not come here in spring when she would have seen them blooming, because the sight of white lilacs always reminded her of the driveway up to her father's house. It had been lined with them. She should be left there now, back in Helsinki, going up to her father's house past the white blooming bushes.

12

Land to Give Away

I HAD meant it about Anna's acre. Thinking of the friends I might not see from year to year made me think of the country habit of sharing, as they had shared at the barn fire that wintry night. I thought about the ad J.R. had inserted in our local paper and his jittery fears. Now since I had permanently quit New York, and found peace, and time, and neighbors, why couldn't my friends eventually, and when they were able, be induced to come out here and share this land?

Often someone down at the Corners would ask why anyone needed forty acres to live on, when none of them were farmed or even let to pasture. The fences have fallen to make gateways for pheasants and woodchucks, or for neighbors' dogs or the neighbors themselves, as they wander in and out of the woods. There is a special pleasure in being unfenced. Woodbine, wild grape, matrimony vines, grow almost anywhere they please. These acres are nearly all wooded hills that could never be profitably farmed—the man and woman who used to live down in the Old Place are testimony to that, or why would she have hired herself out to her neighbors to shuck corn, if she had corn of her own to shuck, and the man getting sick down in the old house, broken with worry over trying to clutch a livelihood out of these hills of gravel, and then trying to reach her in his pain and falling lifeless where this house stands now?

Buck Fife will argue with me, now that I am a lasting part of the community, that I ought to rent the land to some farmer as pasturage for his cattle. Neighbors' cows grazed over the meadow and through the hills before I came, so methodical and thorough in their clipping of leaves from the trees and shearing of the June grass, that woods and meadow looked park-like. In the few years since they have gone, entire trails have disappeared from the woods. Shrubs and saplings in their unmolested growth have overrun and hidden them with the swift rapacity nature always reveals when left to itself. To the city-trained eye, it would be pleasing to see the woods neat again, every leaf from every tree trimmed off in an exact line at the height of a cow's neck's utmost reach. Or the meadow grass held down to a cushiony green. It would be good to rural eyes to see cattle fattening on the land. But also cattle destroy every wildflower; and the life earth wants to nourish is not all one of survival; wanton joy has its place too, and a tremendous patch of nodding shooting stars, or a hilltop starred with Pasque flowers, are as necessary for sustenance as a hundred gallons of milk.

There are the insects and reptiles and mammals earth harbors as lovingly as it harbors men. The ungrazed woods serve, accordingly, as a game and wildlife refuge. Rabbits thrive in the thick undergrowth springing up over old cow trails. So do the pheasant and partridge, returned now since they have learned these acres are a haven—the less dense thickets make admirable ambushes for them to dart from for a quick sortie into Vic Eckstein's grain fields beyond the fences. Deer have been trailed there, foxes, an occasional wolf. Virginia creepers have been planted along the broken fences as cover for ruffed grouse and ringneck pheasants, and snowberry through the woods as winter food for bobwhites, and ninebark for the song-birds, all of these seedlings supplied without charge by the State Conservation Department. Multiflora roses, too, it has supplied, to replace the ugly barbed wire, so that in a few years not only should the fencerows bloom like the pink and white hedgerows of England, but because the roses grow so swiftly into impenetrable thickets, there will never be fences needing mending again. And the bright red rose hips are relished by squirrels, cottontail and snowshoe rabbits, partridge and song-birds alike. So at least the birds and small wild animals are repaid with what is stolen from the cows.

But then the new idea came, mixed up with Anna's acre, and J.R.'s panic, and the sharing of the neighbors at the barn fire. Even with the women and old men haunting Verdi Square, as well as with a few country oldtimers like Sam Jarvis, who lives nearby on two hundred rich acres, his barns full and pros-perous, but his wife, son, and daughter dead, and his only grandson fighting in Korea. There was a time when I saw a lantern moving over his fields and swamp one dark September night, and found him hunting for a lost cow. His farm is iso-lated behind the hills, and none of his neighbors came to help him. His tightfistedness, for which he is famous all over our county, may have been part of the reason. He won't play ball. His grandson has written Bud Devere that when he comes back from Korea, he'll never go near the old man again. His land still produces the most nutritive alfalfa and fattest corn around here, but it does little good when an old man must hunt his lost cow alone.

I also had known what loneliness could be out here, with the sky ripped open by a winter blizzard and the fields and hills exhausted by its fury. And since there are all kinds of earned or unearned loneliness waiting to march beside old age, why shouldn't friends, as each approached what Anna liked to call the autumn, the twilight, of her days, have an acre of land out of these forty, on which to build a small last house? In time there would be a community of them, and no one need ever be alone again. No more wanderers in exile.

Of all these things I talked, in time, with Jane March.

*　　*　　*

Jane was a new neighbor. Paulie's song was ended, and Ed Waldeen had moved away, though that part of the story is for later telling, and now Jane March moved through Paulie's rooms, tended Paulie's gardens. It was good to think of Jane taking care of Paulie's house, piano, books, garden, and trees. Jane was a distant cousin of Paulie's and, when he moved away, Ed offered her the house to live in for almost nothing.

It was lucky for Jane. She was young, alive, with bright, flashing eyes and a candid smile. She was a city woman, from Chicago, loving its noisy, grimy Loop, and its windy beaches and big hotels—just as I had been a city man when I came out here. She did not understand country ways or country sights. The plowed fields, the rolling hills, at first were her enemies. Aunt Dell baffled her, and the Fifes, as they had me, treated her guardedly.

But she was recently widowed—her husband had been one of the first Korean casualties. She had nothing to live on but his pension. She might have found a job, but now Chicago, much as she loved it still, was a haunted place—in this hotel she had danced with Skip, on those El trains she had ridden with him, on that beach she had lain with him. So Ed's offer to her meant more than a house. It was a retreat.

She would not become part of us at the beginning—it was something I could understand well. But a gift of a basket of sweet corn, for which she has an unseemly passion, made her my friend at least. And we had our pasts in common; we understood each other's words, glances; and I had the advantage of having experienced what she was experiencing now—the newness, the lostness, the anger at the mockery. She did not talk about herself. She laughed a great deal. After a few months she had gained several pounds, which worried her, but the pallor was leaving her cheeks—perhaps against her will. Always, through her laughter, I could hear the quiet anger. I seemed to hear the wind blowing through my first winter, down the dark, twisting roads.

We began to see each other often. She liked to talk, as if she were talking something away. She grew to like walking over the hills, listening to stories about my grandfather's place and the family picnics. She was amused at my idea of giving acres away.

"It could be fun," she said. "When you're all old fogeys, you can help take care of each other. That's wonderful! You'll all be ancient and courtly toward each other. And all old, old friends, the best kind! Why shouldn't it work?" Then she frowned. "What if one of your friends decides to turn hermit, once he's safe in these hills?"

She was thinking of herself. There was a familiar cloud in her eyes—once it had been in mine. I caught myself watching her the way Bud used to watch me. Like a doctor studying his patient. Oh Jane, I thought, don't be angry, only wait, it will pass, I can promise, it will. . . .

"Well and good," I answered. "We'll respect each other's privacy, or it would be horrible."

Her forehead was glistening with sweat, as if she were trying to work something out. Oh Jane, only wait. . . . "No borrowing of sugar, to spy on who's having who for dinner?"

"It'll probably be pablum at that age."

She laughed more freely. "You'll need some community projects. I think a joint wading pool would be nice, to cool your sagging old ankles after a summer walk together. You could flood it for a skating rink in winter, with piped-in band music, to waltz by under the moon. Will you all use sleighs?" Then she sobered again. "It needn't be implausible."

"I don't mean it to be."

"Why don't people in the country have cornhusking and quilting bees any more?" she pondered.

"We will."

"And because you're living in the country, why shouldn't ladies dress for dinner?" She was angry again. "After hoeing the garden, I love to get dressed up."

"Our ladies will."

"I think I'll ask for an acre! Just because we're eighty, why shouldn't we still like martinis and a poker game, and have someone to drink and play cards with? I hope we'll quarrel a lot, too—about the size of a fish someone caught back in the 'fifties, or the coming presidential election if we still have 'em, or about who stole whose recipe."

"I hope someone's caught cheating at Skat."

"I hope you listen in on each other's party lines, or there's an unexpected divorce, or an unexpected love affair"—she colored a little—"so we won't forget we're alive! Do you think we could get a gossip, and a snob?"

"I have friends who could work into it."

She was laughing heartily now. "If there's only seventeen of us, I hope someone gives a bridge party for only sixteen. Think of the torture of worrying about who's been left out— it might be you. It really could work out beautifully. Except we're all still young. Why do we worry about it now?"

All at once the cloud was in her eyes again. The despair of her long nights alone, the strangeness and newness. . . .

"By the way," I said quickly, "Aunt Dell wants me to bring you over for supper tonight." Aunt Dell knew nothing about it, but I was certain Jane would be welcome. And I remembered the first time Aunt Dell had knocked on my door. If anything could break Jane down, I knew Aunt Dell's crowded, roisterous, lavish supper table would.

Jane scowled. She looked afraid, and her forehead was glistening again. "Aunt Dell? She seems such an overwhelming character. Are you really friends with people like that? Isn't she sort of a yokel?"

I decided to invite Bud Devere, too.

*   *   *

We say we still are young but we always think we're young. The acres are waiting. I wish I could invite the ladies of Verdi Square. I've even thought about writing J.R. and offering him haven against the bomb. One friend already is here—a retired (and tired) copy writer I had known in Ernie Pollock's office. She has built herself a two-room cottage in the Dog Hollow. Now she'll always be secure. Other friends have staked their claims. With an acre of land, a man owns the world. That is the clearest lesson I have learned.

Then, in time, our last days together will be as rich as our youth. We can do helpful things together, quiet a fear, sustain an illusion, sit by each other's sickbeds, hunt each other's lost cows. And what more can any man ask than to know he will not die alone? I sometimes see a wounded old mallard trying to make his way out of the marshes, or find the trail of a huge woodchuck who must have outlived his span, and wonder what the desolation of old age must be like for them, cast out from their clan. But they are wiser than people, more aloof, preserving their dignity with less tension or pride, and have known a kind of resignation, or at least have had no aspirations, since they were born.

Humans, who defy life with such magnificent hopelessness, as Voltaire did when he shook his fists at the sky and refused to recognize the earthquake that destroyed Lisbon, deserve the gentler way of closing their eyes.

13

The Postals and the Turkey

I WOULD gladly offer an acre to Carrie and Millie Litten if they would take it. If they lived within shouting distance we could stop the business of the postals. I had discovered the convenience of the government postal but should never have mentioned it to them. The glossy surface makes it pleasant to write on. You needn't bother sticking papers in envelopes and getting a gluey mouth. Best of all, you needn't write more than a sentence, because of confined space. The thought of hauling out letter paper and sitting down before that vast blank space, after a day of working outside in real air, becomes as desirable as getting up again and going out to plow a ten-acre field by ox plow. But with a postal a friend can't complain about a quick, brief scrawl—there's no more room on the card. Anyway, cards go off to friends now as often as once a week, when before, with luck and discipline and resentment, I got off a letter once a year.

But I shouldn't have begun to send them to Millie and Carrie. Telephoning them is hazardous enough. They are not confused by the instrument, but it is, I think, confused by them, or at least our operator is, and the phone does strange tricks when they use it, like giving off loud humming sounds or going dead in the middle of a sentence. They will ring you, but then say "Yes?" when you answer, and wait for you to tell them what they called you up about. Or, one time they called, I answered, Millie snapped, "No thank you!" and I heard their receiver banged down. Both were cool to me for several days and I learned later they had been expecting a call that day from an agent impertinent enough to try to sell them a new car.

I had begun instead to communicate with them by postal. I think at first they were offended, because they never answered my messages; or they just threw them away for advertising, though that is unlikely, because no woman of the country is capable of throwing away anything that comes in the mail without studying it first, preferably held up to catch the window light, word for word, including the postmark and *Return In Five Days To*—and *Postmaster: May Open For Inspection*, etc., whether it is a fourth-class-mail circular or the Sears Roebuck catalog; though that of course is never thrown away but stored on a clean special shelf or in a drawer, and rightly, for a later thoughtful study of its marvelous riches.

But before long I began to come back from a few hours spent in the woods hacking away at a blighted tree, or from trying to kill off a big stand of Canadian thistle around the Old Place that threatened to smother the ancient colony of yarrow (nothing I tried would kill the thistle, but a year later the entire patch vanished by itself, re-establishing itself inexorably on Juniper Hill like a wandering biblical tribe)—I'd come back to find a postal stuck under my door, addressed to me, but with no message on the reverse side. Only two signatures: M. Litten, C. Litten. Also the cards never bore a postmark, so they must have been delivered by hand.

It got so I could tell when to expect to find a postal slipped under the door, because if when I got home the old cocker, Shag, wore a miffed look I knew the well-kept Essex had chugged up the hill in my absence. The Littens had never really harmed him, but once Carrie fed him a large sackful of caramels, meaning to be kind. Cockers have very small teeth, but that does not make it less miserable to get caramels tangled in them. And the mouth cavity is so small there's hardly any room to work around in.

Empty postals are disturbing. I finally went to see Carrie and Millie. It was a June day when the red osier, our native northern dogwood—*our*, I had learned to say about all growing things!

—had topped its scarlet spines with mild and pleasant white bloom. The wild crab blooming along the narrow roads was explosively pink and spectacular. Then came the black locust in bloom. It was hard to believe its scent was not manufactured, except for a freshness mingling in it that is not in any woman's perfume. It falls on one more like a barely moving breeze. It is as potent as, but more delicate than, lilac, but also more un-real. Still, completely real. It is a gentle confusion, from the high slim lacelike trees, and in that fading afternoon its scent was so sensuously alive you felt it was laying fingers on you.

Millie was in their garden, planting curly mustard and turnip greens, which they've been advised to eat for their health. But she was planting it two inches deep, giving it little chance to grow, since they don't like it.

"How do you like the weather, Millie?" The warm rare day even made me drop the Miss.

"Hate weather," Millie answered.

"I mean today—"

"Hate any kind," she said, but not unpleasantly. She straight-ened up and shook my hand formally—her hand is small, spotted, and the flesh feels pitifully thin and loose. "Glad you could come," she said, as if I had been invited. "But you're late. Probably spoiled the turkey." She smiled, though, forbear-ingly.

Carrie was on the porch and I noticed how much more stanchly her feet supported her than did Millie's. I was going to ask Millie why I was late, for what, and what turkey was she talking about, but she had already started up toward the house. I thought I heard the veeries singing again.

I followed, climbed the steps to the porch, and flashed a smile to Carrie as bright as hers. Millie took up a watering can and began watering the verdant house plants set along the porch railing, but after the fourth or fifth plant she stopped, since the can was empty from the start anyway, and said amiably to Carrie, "Oh, you already did."

Carrie nodded (but I noticed the earth in the pots: dry as bones) and then turned to me. "Glad you could come for the turkey. Know how you love it, especially with the oyster stuffing."

But Millie had put down the watering can and was holding open the screen door, shooing a few flies back into the house while she waited for me to enter. "Only," she said, "we're having pot roast instead. You won't mind, will you? Lucky thing we remembered. Couldn't have the turkey, naturally, because we couldn't have the oysters. Because there's no 'r' in—" Her thin face grew pained. The screen door slipped from her fingers. "Carrie," she said.

For an instant Carrie frowned, then understood, then nodded. "Clear as your own nose. T-u-r-k-e-y," she spelled and sighed. "There's your 'r' for you plain as day."

Both sisters became crestfallen as we went inside—but I did not bemoan the lack of turkey, even though they might have discovered a host of other "r's" to justify having it and the oyster stuffing. (I wondered how they happened to overlook the "r" in o-y-s-t-e-r itself. Or in s-p-r-i-n-g.) Because from their stove came the aroma of the pot roast simmering in dill shoots and sour cream. They start dill in their cold frame, so that by June they have fresh, foot-high shoots, when the flavor is just subtly beginning to make itself known in the stem and fronds.

"Make yourself comfortable," Carrie said, going into her bedroom to pick mushrooms from her bottom bureau drawer. She really grows them there; the directions said to grow them in a dark damp place, and what's more, they thrive perfectly. She returned, emptied the basket of mushrooms into the old-fashioned kind of dull metal sink, and began cleaning them with swipes of a moist cloth. Millie was busy with spaetzle to go with the roast. There was a silence, unusual around their kitchen. I thought they might still be disgruntled about the turkey, but it was only a springlike somnolence. It had lulled them, content with their skillet and big spoons. Now was my time, about the postals. Busy with their mushrooms and batter, they might be caught sufficiently off-guard to give a reasonable answer.

"I've been getting the postals you've been leaving under the door."

Millie gave me an appreciative glance. "Glad you told us about them. We send them to all our friends now. Saves time. Cuts down phone bills, too." Their local phone bill is an undeviating $2.86 per month, and they have never been known to make a toll call. Regarding their Essex as something like a horse and wagon, they reason it is cheaper to drive long-distance than telephone it.

I mentioned that, nevertheless, they said nothing on the cards.

"Don't want the whole post office knowing our business, do we?" Carrie asked, giving the mushrooms a shake in the frying pan.

I said that wasn't likely, since they didn't mail them.

Millie shrugged. "Much better this way. Delivering those postals ourselves, we get to see our friends as well as write to them. Kills two birds."

Carrie, at the stove, nodded approvingly at Millie's wisdom. I didn't ask anything more.

Supper was a gentle, murmury affair, and they both took good care as always to heap the best and biggest portions of everything on my plate. They can make you feel monarchial at the supper table. After dishes were done, I knew they would want to play cards, but I had excuses ready. Only a few weeks before, trapped into another canasta game with them, I had suggested three-handed bridge instead, since they bid slams in all card games anyway. We played with two decks, dealing with one while the other was shuffled and placed in readiness beside the next dealer. Halfway through a rubber Carrie picked up a new hand, but by mistake picked up the full deck waiting at her elbow instead of the hand dealt to her. She spread the fifty-two cards like a monstrous fan in her sturdy fingers, studied them briefly, and interrupted her cheerful chatter only long enough to pass.

The pot roast and mushrooms and spaetzle would leave any-one in spirits to match the June day—or rather now, the June evening, in which the black-locust perfume grew stronger than before, championing its way above the other scents, as if only in dark night did it really exert itself. There was no moon—its absence seemed to bring the locusts into dominion. They ruled alone, without planets, stars, sun, earth. They could be seen standing in ink against the lesser ink of the sky, light-stemmed, faintly frivolous, but true queens of these few hours, not with-out evil in their own terrible ascension, having obliterated even the moon. I was enjoying their black, slim reign, myself rele-gated to the back porch, while Millie and Carrie clinked and clattered away in their lighted kitchen beyond the open door-way, in the comfortable hollowness a warm spring night pro-duces. It was no night for cards.

Then I heard one of them lift the hood of their sewing ma-chine, where their cards are kept. Tonight was Friday. In all the villages around, the stores keep open until nine o'clock on Friday nights, and farmers and their wives and all their chil-dren, it seems a dozen apiece, all with popsicles, crowd through the big new supermarkets that have muscled into even the smallest towns. It is a meeting time, one of the best times in the country, everybody looking prosperous, wheeling carts through the stores, the wire baskets piled mountainously high with groceries, until you would think no one grew anything on his own farm.

The young men crowd the taverns and young girls walk by outside them in pairs, their steps lingering, their eyes looking as if they were a thousand miles away, but their hearts already inside the taverns beside the raucous men, already kissing with them on dark meadows under a starry sky. Friends and neigh-bors greet, smile, yell, laugh, and chatter at one another, kids run into the street and get rescued, women lose their purses, farmers test a new tractor, and for an evening at least the town grows complete and self-contained.

From behind me in the kitchen came the riffling of cards. "I've got to run over to Dousman," I called through the doorway. "I just remembered—no groceries at home. Lucky the stores are open."

No protest. The cards were put away. Millie and Carrie came out to the porch smiling. Their steps even had quickened. "Need a few supplies too," Carrie said. "Not enough in the house to feed a mouse. A body could starve." I could see straight into their pantry, piled to the ceiling with jars, cans, buckets, and tubs. They preserve and pickle all summer long, wild asparagus from along the fencelines, chickens, pig's feet, wild strawberries, wild plum and crab, quinces, elderberries for pies, every vegetable that grows. They store every nut that falls to the ground. They make chutneys, pickalillies, chowchows. They drown nasturtium seeds in vinegar to make capers. They still store eggs in waterglass in winter. (But never eat them. "Why not?" I once asked. "Would you?" Millie snapped back.) I knew there was twice as much more stored in their vegetable cellar downstairs as in the pantry. A body could starve in their house only after a year of gorging first. "So we might as well all ride over together," Carrie said, and already had her purse.

"In my car," I said quickly.

I was surprised that they agreed again. I knew their shrewd and native good taste made them distrust convertibles, but tonight they climbed into my car without a murmur. Perhaps because it was spring. I know they enjoyed it. Dousman was only three miles and we only had to stop twice on the way. Once because Millie had to remove herself from the back seat beside Carrie to the front seat beside me—she said it was too windy back there (with the top up, on a breezeless night) but I think she just wanted people to see her riding in someone else's car. And once because Carrie, in an abrupt flurry, insisted the car was in flames. I jammed the brakes. We all jumped out. I looked over the car from bumper to bumper. Everything was fine.

"What made you think the car was burning?"

"Heard it on the radio last night," Carrie answered flatly. Millie, too, by the side of the dark road in the glow of the tail light, was white. "They fasten things on your magneto."

"Who? What?"

" 'Dragnet.' Thugs. Gangsters," Carrie said. "Sporty cars like this, they're always crossing wires or dropping things in the gas chamber."

"Tank," I said curtly. Jamming the brakes, I'd worn half the rubber off the tires.

"In the gas chamber," Carrie repeated stubbornly.

Suddenly Millie wore a sly, girlish grin unusual for her. "Say that again," she said to me.

"Say what?"

"Tank."

"Tank," I said.

"Tank you, too," Millie answered, with a gale of laughter as she crawled back into the car, in both of which acts she was shortly joined by Carrie. There is sometimes a raspy toughness in Millie's laugh, despite her small size. And after that, like two giddy schoolgirls, they chuckled and bounced, both of them, on the front seat beside me now all the way into Dousman.

They love the supermarkets. They gasp with slight shock and resentment as they go by the electric eye that opens the door, but then go back and try it a few more times, until they can beat the beam and open the door by hand the way normal doors should be opened. Inside, each takes a cart, and I've seen Millie look in uncommunicative abstraction at the kind kids can ride in. They make a tour of the store filling their carts sky-high with everything from the shelves, perhaps imagining they are somebody else, for then they make a second tour putting everything back, invariably in the wrong places, canned corn in the ice-cream freezer, cheese among the fresh vegetables. Then they begin a third tour for the things they really want.

This night, when they needed groceries to stave off starvation, Millie bought a grapefruit and Carrie bought a small cellophane bag of gumdrops. Nothing more. They began trailing after me, critically eying every purchase I made, casting each other derisive, mute glances, as if there were nothing remarkable about the contents of *their* carts, and giving each other more of the glances I was not supposed to see when I bought a big rib roast and then a jar of martini onions.

"Having a party?" Carrie asked.

"Yes."

"Oh," Carrie said.

"Oh," Millie said. "Big party?"

"Big party," I said.

"Too bad," Carrie said. "We were planning on inviting *you*."

"When?" I hadn't said what night.

"That night," Carrie said baldly.

I began laughing. "Why don't I treat you to a soda?" My eyes fell on Leo Guernan's tavern across the street from the supermarket. "Or how about a beer, girls?"

We had one. They climbed up on stools at the bar, and politely took off their hats. It is hard to say what wisdom and strength you can often feel emanate from them, all unknown to them. It just felt good, sitting there with them, drinking beer, looking at the loud young people, listening to the juke box.

I don't think they had ever been in a bar before, but they are by no means prudish and each drank half her beer. They tried everything—the peanuts, the pretzels. They enjoyed the juke box. Millie brought out two pennies from her purse, and Carrie three. Then they asked me for a dime. They had Leo exchange the dime for two nickels. By that time someone else had put a nickel in the juke box. So they gave me a nickel, Carrie slipped a nickel into her purse, and Millie slid the five pennies into hers. Somehow they'd made a nickel and still had music. They thanked me for the music, and jiggled their feet contentedly. Afterward they even tried investigating the ladies' room, from which they returned to tell Leo bluntly he ought to wash the writing off his walls. Then they blushed. Not because of the scribbled walls, but because, of course, Leo couldn't go in there.

On the way home they hummed softly to themselves, though each a separate tune. It was slow and restful. Such are spring nights all over the world, I thought. We drove under the tent of black locust perfume, all in the front seat. Back at their house they were reluctant to get out. When they did, they left their gumdrops and grapefruit behind and took a bag of my groceries with them. And somehow they looked like young girls coming home from the fair and I could not ask to have it back, the groceries, nor the reverie on their faces, nor their gentle humming.

I went to the door with them, when Millie abruptly darted inside and returned with a sealed blank envelope. They looked expectant, so I opened it and found a postal inside. It was addressed to me, and was dated a week before, and this time at least bore a message on its reverse side. *We are having turkey for supper Friday. We hope you can come.*

"But that's tonight," I began. But they were looking so pleased, Millie so frail, and Carrie plump and a little taller. And at the same time Millie said, "Hope you can make it!"

I drove home, wondering—not about anything in particular, though. It was comfortable. The locusts were glimmering all around. They stood like dark smiling queens.

14

Wine from These Grapes

FENNEL, rosemary, rue. These were new names, country names—names that had no city life, except dried and stored in bottles on dusty grocery store shelves. But here they were living names, blowing and sunny. I learned new ones from Aunt Dell each spring. Borage, sweet basil, thyme. Coltsfoot, bible leaf. Chervil. Chives and mint and sage. Comfrey, costmary, ginger. The names have the ring of couplets out of Shakespeare. Pleurisy root and campion. Lad's love and maiden's ruin. Holy basil, which is sacred to the Vishnu-Brahmans—"But there ain't none living around here, ainna?" Aunt Dell tells you brightly. Agrimony, which her much-thumbed catalog says is "not now much used but grown for its oldtime reputation," and Culver's physic, whose roots, Aunt Dell says cautiously, are used "for a remedy." Germander, used for magic. Woodruff, which gives new May wine its glow.

There is nothing quaint about a bed of herbs under Aunt Dell's hands. In all her evanescent garden, these are the plants that thrive for her, possibly because of their ultimate realistic

destiny in soups or stews. She uses herbs so naturally and relentlessly that they seem her staff of life. She grows them as
others grow cabbages or carrots. Each spring she brings up a
few old coffee cans filled with seedlings or slips of a half-dozen
new kinds to be stuck into the ground, nursed along, waited
over patiently, and then experimented with.

She is also the one who can storm through the woods on a
sunny, blowy, fresh spring day, basket on her sturdy arm, or
wallow and thresh along the edge of the marsh, to return with
a basketful of unheard-of greens to make the best salad ever
eaten. It's like a short holy season, those few sudden hot days
in late April or early May, when Aunt Dell appears, with two
or three baskets and wearing rubber boots on her long strong
feet, and heads off toward the marsh. I have tried going along,
but can't find the things she finds. She has an enchanted eye for
spotting edible shoots and sprouts that you would never have
dreamed of eating. She plucks them from the earth like a crafty
sorceress, her broad face benign as the day. Her favorite find is
fiddleheads, the shoots of wild ferns just as they are beginning
to unfurl. It is strange what things men will eat, but then, Aunt
Dell points out, who was the first man to try nibbling on the
peculiar misshapen underground growth called the potato?

She fries the fiddleheads, after she has coated them in fine
crumbs, or cooks them like asparagus to drown in a sauce. She
is not a fancy cook, and never cooks by recipe; she just cooks, as
she just "makes" a dill crock. She is never even very surprised
at what wonderful things come out of her oven or off her stove.
She has a range as huge and lusty and shining as herself. It looks
like a hotel range. But then, her family is hotel size, comple-
mented by the neighbors or tramps or wayfarers she is always
hauling in to fill her already crowded table.

She and Carrie and Millie are spoken of as amiable enemies,

who would not dream of exchanging a recipe. But the Littens won't; and Aunt Dell can't. She improvises on her stove, so there is no recipe. It's the same way with her salads. She returns with a healthy wave of her big hand down the wooded hill, and in her baskets might be anything—pale cool green, and lettuce green, and apple green, and fir green shoots, and small crisp leaves all in a mess, smelling of damp earth and spring and cold water. Dandelion shoots, of course, and tiny lemony-flavored sprouts of sheep sorrel, which other farmers pray not to find because it means their soil is dead, if the sorrel is rampant. And young wild chicory and wild leek and the roots of earth apple and slender shoots of milkweed and a dozen others I can't name. And morels, the tan, honeycombed, delicate mushrooms. She can find morels like a dowser drawn to hidden water. Morels cooked in fresh butter, and a salad of green sprouts and shoots, and a chunk of homemade rye bread. That is the kind of lunch Aunt Dell will set before you as carelessly as if it were cold beans.

Over one of those lunches you sit and talk about her kiddo Buss, the one that should be "straggled," who, when she asked him to throw her down the steps his dirty pants for the washing, did. That is, he was in them, and landed in her stomach and, big as she is, knocked her clear the wind right out. Or you worry about neighbors like the Waldeens or the vandals who tipped over the stones in the cemetery or the kids racing hotrods through the village. Or the talk gets around to books, of which Aunt Dell reads plenty, or the new electric organ they're raising money for in Jerusalem Church. Outside the sun is beating on new green grass, and there are still more morels, flavored with last year's basil in the frying pan, and you get to wondering what more anyone could ever want of life.

Aunt Dell, one time, had my same thoughts. She sighed, leaning back comfortably in her chair. "Rich, ainna?" she smiled.

*   *   *

The herbs in the garden were father to the vinegar. The vinegar came from wine. The wine would not have happened were it not for the abundance of grapes. They are the wild, purple kind, and grow like jungle vines in the woods, or along fences, or up trees, or down ravines, or along the railroad tracks. The trunks are like thick petrified snakes and the tendrils reach out with numb but deft assurance. The tropistic grip of the seasoned tendril around a barb wire or tree branch is appalling in its tenacious power. Then the grapes come, and I find myself wishing my fox had not vanished from the woods. They hang so lush, heavy, prodigal. But the songbirds gorge on them, chattering with full beaks, with enough left over for larger grouse and quail, and cottontail rabbits, and an occasional deer strayed down along the railroad tracks from up north.

And still enough left over for man and jelly and grapejuice and wine. Buck Fife suggested the winemaking. Earlier during the summer I had found a wine press at a farm auction, and it sat uselessly in the kitchen, looking rustic, which is not the function of a press. Buck mentioned as much.

"Got the damn thing. Might as well use it. Your place is lousy with grapes."

He was up helping restore some asphalt shingles a wind and thunderstorm had blown loose. He kept talking down at me from the roof.

"Tomorrow," he called, clenching shingle nails in his mouth. Coupled with the scowl of his natural reticence, it made him look like a young pokerfaced walrus.

"Tomorrow what?" I called back.

"I'll bring the family up. Pick the damn grapes. Use your damn press. Make wine." He spit out the nails and grinned. "Maybe we can get May to come along." His sister May was the reckless dancer.

"Oh, fine," I laughed. "Maybe I can get Aunt Dell to fix us a big meal and we'll make it a party."

"Wow," Buck said.

"Regular harvest festival. We'll press the grapes with our bare feet."

"Not May," Buck said. "She's finicky."

The whole family came up early the next day, a Sunday, and Aunt Dell came, bringing Tom along, and the twins, and Buss, who lived up to expectations by practicing on birds or friends alike with his slingshot, picking only what grapes his mouth could hold, and then going off quietly to a corner of the woods to spend the rest of the afternoon digging a bear pit—for people to fall into. Aunt Dell fixed a pork roast shrouded in fresh herbs, and baked beans and macaroni, and began cleansing about a ton of several kinds of lettuces to fix with sour cream while all the rest of us went out along the fences and through the clearings in the woods.

The Fifes had brought bushel baskets along, dozens, for the picking; and jugs, dozens, for the juice. We were going to split the harvest. The kids were wonderful. In bare feet they shinnied up the thick trunk vines or the trees that supported them like voluble monkeys. May came, but she brought along a new boy friend from Genesee, and they stayed behind on the terrace. Love did indeed make her seem finicky. She was all dressed up, but contributed her part of the courtship by bringing a book along and reading it all afternoon, while Dick, the friend, sat next to her, impressed and bored, tossing peanuts to some chip-munks.

We picked bushels. Buck's mother picked the most. Every-one got grapes in his hair and stains on his hands and face. Buck's mother, tall and gaunt, somehow got purple tears of them down her burnt cheeks, but the tears had come from laughing. Then the women washed the grapes and picked them over (not May; she never looked up from her book) and the men began the pressing. The whole operation managed to stain the kitchen, as well, bright purple. The men were bare-chested and barefooted. Aunt Dell fixed supper on tables out-doors. May's cultural leanings grew oppressive when she should have been showing the symptoms of love, and someone stacked the record player with Billie Holiday and Billy Eckstine records, and culture fell from May like a G-string. She jumped up and began dancing with Dick in the living room and the festival really got going.

Impatient, we bought wine, too. It loosened up everybody, and sun-red or sun-brown or sun-black celebrants, depending on previous degrees of exposure, and all purple-flecked, filled the kitchen and terrace and shoved around the outdoor supper tables under the trees.

But around sundown people quieted unexpectedly. I didn't know what was happening, but voices began to lower, the kids were called in from their ball game in the meadow, May and her friend Dick shut off the record player. Mrs. Fife put on a clean apron, and from all over, from the fields and under the trees and around the supper table, people picked up their chairs and brought them to the terrace.

"What's up?" I asked Buck.

He motioned toward the terrace. "Don't get scared." He looked nervous and sheepish, but also a little defensive. "Ma's old man. Got those old ideas." He jerked a thumb sidewise.

And his thumb led me to Mrs. Fife's father, who is purebred Welsh, a small, immaculate man, but with muscles of iron for all his age, and with a grave, tired face. All day he had worn a hat but now he took it off and put it on a stone behind him. He stood at the edge of the terrace, silhouetted, the evening dying contentedly behind him, the meadow stretching like a flaming sea; and then he began, without any preamble, to give an honest-to-God, short, pleasant sermon. He gestured little and spoke exactly like a plain old man speaking earnestly and imploringly to all his children and grandchildren and neighbors and friends, speaking with authority only because he was the eldest, about the fruits of the vineyard and how grateful we were to receive them.

I hadn't expected a sermon on this day of mild carousing, and his even voice made me fidget. Buck saw me, blushed, winked, and suddenly looked angry because he had. But the others seemed accustomed to it. They listened carefully, and yet casually. The old voice went on with a kind of friendly gratitude to God for filling the vines and giving us hands to strip them. (*Out here you'll learn gratitude,* I remembered my mother had said.) It wasn't fancy talk or inspired, but he meant it. It made you begin to understand religion, with his words coming clearly through the mild evening air, and a few bushel baskets of unpressed grapes still sitting around, and all the ruddy, tired faces, and the scent of grapes on the air, and then the sky itself slowly darkening to a wild-grape color.

Aunt Dell looked morose but happy with her arms folded under her apron; and the kids, though growing impatient, squatted as respectfully as they could; and Mrs. Fife listened and kept nodding to things her father said; and Buck scowled but listened; and May sat with head tilted and one hand placed carelessly in her boy friend Dick's hand; until finally Mrs. Fife's father said Amen and reached down and put his hat on again.

Then the children rushed back to the meadow to try and finish their ball game before the darkness got too deep, but the others just lingered with a curious relaxation around the terrace. Their voices sounded calmer and richer.

"Do you have this every Sunday? It's nice," I said to Mrs. Fife.

It was nice—but I meant much more. I had the feeling her father had spoken words that a long time had struggled inside me, but had never found their way out. I was thinking, what if I had never come out here, what if the shattering sleepless nights had not driven me to these hills, that now in the dying light looked holy, what if Ernie Pollock had saved my job? I

would never have known the glory of a bushel basket crammed with wild grapes. I would never have seen this man's bowed head. I would never have had this awesome slugging in my heart.

Then, as quickly, it grew calm. "It's nice," I repeated to Mrs. Fife.

She nodded and smiled fondly toward her father. "He thinks we're just making grape juice."

*   *   *

That Sunday, too, I developed an especial respect for Buck's younger brother of thirteen because of a story his mother told me. The Fifes, three-fourths Welsh, are a tight-lipped, tenacious, and indomitable clan. The day before, the boy had been helping his father replace a six-inch beam that, through rot at one end, had come loose in the barn just under the haymow. The boy held the beam in place while Mr. Fife tried to wedge its end fast again, and in the operation the beam slipped and dropped on the boy's head. Father and son exchanged glances but no word came from the boy's lips. They set to work again but once more the beam slipped. I like to imagine that this time the boy at least rubbed his head, even if he did remain silent. But the third time the heavy beam fell on his head the boy was, at last, moved to comment.

"Father," he said, "my head hurts."

*   *   *

The grape juice was put to ferment in crocks, half here, half in the Fifes' cellar. There was nothing to do but wait. By midwinter Buck's turned to good mellow wine, as clear as burgundy, but a little darker. Mine turned to vinegar.

To Buck and his family, this was the comic event of the century. Ten gallons of translucent, ruby vinegar. I am invited down to the Fifes' occasionally for a glass of wine, and once Mr. Fife did suggest they ought to send a half gallon home with me, but nothing came of it. I expect that to a Welshman one's produce is his produce. No sense horsing around about it.

But what might have been gall, sweetened next summer when the herbs ripened for picking. The vinegar had a rich, fruity flavor, and Aunt Dell was the one who sensibly put two and two together. Rife under the hot sun were the tarragon, sweet basil, dill, mint, borage, summer savory.

"Look, mister," Aunt Dell said cheerfully. "What's herbs for, ainna? Just to sit in gardens or to sit inside bottles?"

"You mean we could make herb vinegar that easily?"

"Self-evident," she answered grandly.

On the rubbish heap were enough old bottles, too, of nice shapes and colors. Aunt Dell's strong fingers went to work picking an assortment of herbs, cramming them lustily down bottle necks, while I filled them up from the vinegar jugs. Then she set them all in a row along window ledges, to steep for a few weeks in the sun, a prismatic row, the herbs floating in the dark seas like undulant weeds.

It turned out even better than Buck's hoard of wine. There is still extra vinegar in the basement to try out each year with new and other herbs, each changing the vinegar's flavor as subtly as a pebble in a stream will change the course of water, that faintly, but that positively, too. In some bottles Aunt Dell had poked just dill. Or mint. Or tarragon. Or a mixture of basils. But best of all was one of dill and mint and garlic. It was good to see and smell all the bottles, the vinegar from the wine from the grapes from the land and the herbs from the same yielding land.

There was so much, enough for neighbors and friends. I made the mistake of taking some up to the Waldeens. In a way they had been almost forgotten, as they wanted. Their hermit fancies had gradually been accepted by the countryside. It was two whole years since their door had closed, and their neighbors had tacitly agreed to let them live in the seclusion they asked for. Having made that agreement, the next logical step was in a sense courteously to forget them, except perhaps to wonder a little about them as you drove by their house. You'd see them in the yard, planting new shrubs or hoeing in the vegetable garden, or Ed driving the truck in from the field, or Paulie putting up awnings or taking them down again, stretching her small frame so high on top of a perilously high ladder, always reminding me of the way she had stretched toward the sky and life on the hill that one November afternoon, and you waved, and Ed and Paulie waved back, and you were glad when distance separated you again because of the chill such mechanical courtesies left in you.

As I drove over that day with the vinegar, I was struck by the desertion around their house, though it was a blistering day after a week of maddening heat, this coming on top of nearly a month of drought, and it is no surprise perhaps that an empty and noiseless place, under a broiling sun, seems about a thousand times as empty and dead of noise. It was exactly the opposite of the vitality and chattering you always expected from Paulie.

Their doors were locked when I tried them, front and back and side, the awnings down, shades drawn inside, the garage was empty, the barns locked, cattle gone, a bed of zinnias ready to bud were a tangled, gray, burnt, lifeless mass. I remember thinking that this was a patch of flowers that properly belonged in Aunt Dell's garden.

I went to look at some of the new trees. That spring, Paulie had surprised everyone by a sudden gay flurry in which she set out over a dozen blossoming trees—hawthorn, flowering plum, crab, bronze-leaved *Prunus pissardi*. Paulie did this, not Ed, digging with spades taller than she was and staking and fertilizing and watering. You could see her as you drove past. Whatever has happened, you thought, there is still the future worth planning for, a future in which the trees would grow high and blossom. But now the Waldeens had gone away and left her trees.

The leaves of the thin trees were already curling and fading in the drought. I found a watering can behind their garage, and carried can after can to each tree, which the baked earth slurped up noisily. I kept looking at their house. They must have gone away on a trip, I thought. Indeed, they were on a trip. Later I found out where, and what a sad, stupendous journey it was, a kind of farewell tour that ended in a hospital room that Paulie had reserved—for herself—even before the trip began. But she took the trip with Ed. There was a song of life inside her and she simply wouldn't stop singing it.

15

Reign's End

SHAG, or Artemis Flanders, had arrived during that awakening summer of the year when Bud first drove me along the Willow Road. Often, watching the love of country life grow in him as he discovered a new field, a new clump of hazel thicket to rest under, a new pond to wade in, I longed to cry out to him, Go on, Shag, go it! Yip all you want. I know how you're feeling, boy . . . !

He was a city dog, a black cocker, nine years old when he came here. He had never before raced over hills or across meadows. All his life his black ears had dragged moodily along city sidewalks. He had always been leashbound, never free— like my fox!—but always city-confined like a factory worker or shop clerk, trapped to pad along airless streets, never to see trees or skies, never to yelp and race happily to freedom.

He belonged to a friend whose city-shriveled landlord ordered him either to move or get rid of Shag—Shag had once or twice had accidents on the hallway carpeting. It was the gas chamber for Shag, unless. . . . And out here were forty acres of space and air and freedom.

He was a lonely, aloof dog, and yet affectingly dependent once he got used to you. But still independent—on going outside, he must stop at the door, to reflect on the day, but also to let you know that if he went out, he was going of his own free will. Both his former master and mistress had worked, and his nine years of days had been spent alone, locked up in an apartment, curled in a sofa corner. I don't think he had ever seen the country. He didn't want to come out here. But after the first few moody days, when he decided to explore the outside, he knew exactly what to do about a hazelnut thicket. He yipped, tore into it, sniffed a hundred fabulous smells he had never known existed to be sniffed, and reappeared a half hour later snagged and snarled and grinning. In an instant he had become a dog.

A cocker has much power and stamina in its small body (having originally been bred as hunter, not pet) and once Shag took to the fields, these bloomed in him overnight. Only he never learned how to hunt. With eerie screams, he would race through the junipers and oaks, circling for an hour through the tearing underbrush of raspberries and young sumacs and the twin sisters birds have seeded through the woods. But he never caught anything nor even flushed a bird or chipmunk, until you wondered what he thought he was hunting. Final, humiliating proof of it came with a rabbit in the meadow. The startled rabbit hopped past Shag, heading south, while Shag marched past the rabbit, heading north, within two feet of each other. But Shag never saw the rabbit. He kept marching blithely home, no doubt wishing he had something to hunt.

He took over the house, the woods and fields, of course; became master. He never liked other dogs, perhaps because he had never known any, and was game to tackle any dog, any size, that strayed onto his acres from a neighboring farm. There was such a frenzied viciousness in his attacks on these alien dogs twice his size, that I think there must have been some unknown terror in it—he seemed, plainly, to be fighting for survival, though I never learned what in his life had conditioned him to such desperation. But with men he was gentle, if indifferent. He quickly developed a one-man attachment that one would expect from a much bigger, more virile dog.

*   *   *

It was a blow, then, when Ida was introduced a year later into the house where Shag ruled. Suddenly the kitchen floor, the slopes of the hills, the meadow with its tall dry grasses, were not his alone any more. Ida, a two-year-old water spaniel, was the gift of another friend, who had found her on sale while driving through a nearby town, and she was penned in a six-foot pen, and she was such a frisky dog, and unhappy in her pen, etc., and here were these forty acres, etc., etc. . . .

But it was impossible not to love Ida at first sight, with her russet topknot, shaggy ears, and inquiring eyes. Irish spaniels, too, are great hunters, and the woods and marshes are their natural habitat. But she is also part clown. Though we gave her a rug in the back hallway, she sleeps only in the woodbin. She had a fondness for chewing doorknobs. She chased airplanes. As a watchdog she barked only at the absence of strangers; to strangers she wagged a welcome. She barks at trees, birds, Carrie and Millie, but never at tramps. A favorite sport, if undetected, is to drag smoldering logs from the fireplace and lay them on the carpets. She is a rich reddish brown, her coat tightly curled; she has long blowsy ears and wears the topknot with the style of a French poodle. It is a warm, keen, brown-eyed face. She looks a little like the not very ferocious lion in Rousseau's "Sleeping Gypsy." She is a monument of kindly watchfulness like that lion—when you bathe, she hangs her head stone-still over the rim of the tub, watching to make certain you don't go under.

And, though eight years younger, took it upon herself to be Shag's protector. Don't wander too near the railroad tracks. Don't stay out in the cold too long. Come on, let's get back inside the house. Run, beat it, here comes a car. (Though of late she has taken to sitting plumb in the middle of the driveway, yelping an eager but unbudgable greeting to cars trying to get up the hill.) It was always Ida who issued these warnings, amiability and trustworthiness itself, and because she was a female Shag accepted them. In his way, he grew fond of Ida. He would lie still for an hour while Ida gently chewed burdock burs and the sticky pellets of viper's bugloss out of his dragging ears. They were usually together, though Shag rebuffed any attempt at play. That was far behind him. He'd tag after Ida to the woods, but with no display of affection or need. That he saved only for his master.

It was Shag and Ida who were destined to become parents. From their issue was to come the story of one dog's cruel, if unwitting, torment of another. In his third year out here, another lazy summer was ending for Shag. The September mornings were deceitful with warmthless sunlight, and Ida was weaning her puppies. But much more was ending for Shag that I did not know. Certain marks of age had begun to show. He had grown a slight tumor, though not malignant, on his chest. His coat, despite brushing, was losing its glisten, a dull paintlike black replacing the once-ebony sheen. His ears, hopelessly matted and burred from treks in the woods, had needed repeated shearings, and they dangled now like frowzy tassels. His chin went hoary. In the past months, a black bald spot had spread on his shank.

Surely nothing more should be asked of him, who had already lived so fully—by human reckoning, he would be past seventy. So he was never asked to play dead again, by a kind of mute agreement between all who knew him, or was ordered to sit up or bark for his food, or retrieve his much-chewed rubber ball. Ida as much as possible was kept out of his way. He was taken outside only when he asked for it (having begun to spend most of his time in his own bed in the kitchen corner), waddling then, not racing as before, to the door, seating himself on his bulky spaniel haunches and waiting with upraised head, tongue lopping sidewise through black lips, eyes blinking, until the door was opened. He rose to his four feet then, turned about, hesitated with bowed head, stepped outside.

But he did not greet the meadows and hills with the noisy yelps of former days. I think now perhaps the attention showered on Ida during her pregnancy and motherhood had already begun to sour him. Outside, he greeted neither September rain nor amber sunshine with expectant yips. He went calmly, no longer even bristling at sight of farmers' dogs on his land, and after plodding around the yard for a while simply looked up at whomever might be outside with him as if asking, Well, can I go back in? It was usually young Tom Dell, who will always take care of others, of anything that moves on wings or four feet and needs his help, who would be outside with him. Tom would try to make him play. Shag never noticed him. A last none-too-interested survey of life outside, the trees, the dun-colored valley, even a dull glance toward his most mortal enemy, King, a sleek Doberman from the next farm, ferreting near the garbage heap, and Shag retraced his steps to the house, sniffing at places he had watered on the outward journey, halt-

ing stock-still and momentarily preoccupied with an autumn
leaf on the terrace, but giving it no more than that moment's
paralyzed glance. The last few feet he even quickened his pace,
as though in haste to put the outside world behind him, padding inside with a rapid, thuddy step. A lap from his water
basin, and one still-easy leap into his bed. Twirling himself
around, scuffing up the rag blanket, sniffing—*the past days in
the hills, the high sweet meadow grass, the warm flaky earth!*—
until his snout settled on a feathery, extended forepaw, all men,
even his master, forgotten, eyes shut quick as a trigger, already
sleeping, dreaming, sometimes twitching, uncurling abruptly
and curling again, sometimes faintly yipping without opening
his eyes, or more rarely panting, or even making a low whinny-
ing sound. Were those dreams, then, of Ida and her new
puppies?

He began to sleep insatiably. But it was much more than
age. Later when the humiliation came on him it made his
wakeless nights only more grotesque. If only that sleep might
have increased daily, winding tighter and tighter until it wound
too tight, the end of all painful waking, only sleep forever. . . .

*　　*　　*

Shag fathered Ida's first litter not by design. There is no
beauty in a dog's passion. It is an atavistic, embarrassing season, when emotions and intentions are laid bare as a bald head.
For eighteen to twenty-one days there is unabated howling,
inviting, barking, beckoning, answering, joined by a dozen dogs
that come from a mile around to beleaguer the house. Ida was
kept locked unhappily in the basement. Shag panted before
her door. The visiting dogs, reluctant to go home even at night,
slept on the terrace furniture, attacked the garbage heap,
strewed the yard, pawed at the doors, always answered by Ida's

yowls. It is nature on the loose, and bawdy as an oldtime whore.

Springtime for Ida, perhaps, but it gave her positive ideas of her own, who had only been docile and obedient before. Shag had been continent all his years. How they reached each other I don't know, but I slept peacefully one night and awoke with a disturbing awareness of the peace in which I had slept. Of course, there had been no barking. On the kitchen floor (and I don't know how Ida loosed the hinge on her door) Shag and Ida slept together, snoring, desire fulfilled.

No glimmer of motherhood or awakening responsibility ever brightened Ida's eyes in the next few weeks. Shag went on his separate way again, aloof and indifferent. But after a month a strange, wonderful detachment came to Ida. After all, she had begun a new world of her own. She seemed to know it. She grew self-sufficient, needing no man or master. She raced in wild circles around the meadow for a half hour at a time, engulfed in her own solitary enjoyment, or instinctive knowledge that she needed exercise, or whatever it was. The incredible instincts uncurled from sleep. She looked wise, as she sat evenings on the terrace, gazing far into space.

I was building a dog house, hammering against time. Ida watched with laconic disdain. It had been reassuring to read in a dog book that her puppies would not be too mismatched, because both Irish and cocker spaniels come from the same ancestral breed. Ida, the book also said, would know how to make her nest before the puppies came, and would make it where she pleased. Hence, her laconic amusement at my sawing and pounding.

The puppies were born on the dot and without need of anyone. Though "on the dot" is perhaps not apt. More specifically, on the back seat of the car. She always rides along for the mail, and near the railroad bridge I heard a soft whimper. When I turned around, there was a brown blind puppy on the seat next to Ida, looking exactly like a small Ida. Ida blinked, looked around vaguely, not at all like a mother in labor; but then stretched herself out along the seat and went back to work. Racing home, scooping up the puppy, depositing it in the dog-house under a cool arching tree—it was in vain. She ignored the puppy and everything else, except to scratch at the kitchen screen door until she was let inside, where she made a beeline for the woodbin, no doubt decided on long ago. She let out one bark of splendid and terrifying magnitude, and then settled down to wait patiently until her firstborn was brought to her, when she began cleaning it with a woeful concern.

This was high noon. At twelve-twenty, the second appeared. Twelve-thirty, number three. She was calm, unafraid, a little mystified, lying stretched out so quietly, a wise patience in her eyes, her head resting against the woodbin wall. As each puppy wriggled out, it began its awesome, blind, instinctual march around to Ida's teats, as if it had been given prenatal directions. Ida remained gentle until the seventh, last puppy was born in late afternoon. Four brown, like herself; three black, like Shag. Shag sniffed once or twice at these latter three with mild but no proprietary interest. But once the last was born, instinct burst through the wall of abating pain and ferocity awakened. Ida snarled at anyone approaching the nest. She bit Tom's hand when he tried to freshen her water bowl. More surprisingly, while she was gobbling soup meat, one of the puppies wobbled and wriggled too near the chunk of meat and with one clout Ida sent the puppy sprawling a yard away. The puppy blindly but unerringly wriggled back and Ida yanked it by its tail under-neath her, where it belonged. So ended, it seemed, the first les-son. . . . Was it really the instinctual knowledge that a puppy cannot digest meat?

Once or twice more Shag wandered too near the woodbin, but not with interest, merely passing it en route to his own bed, hesitating, one paw upraised and his head turned away, a look of deep moroseness in his downcast eyes, and Ida sent up such a thunder of protection that Shag took a slinking leap to his bed, shrunken to the size of a beetle. And did not know how his doom was on him already.

In a few days Ida's gentleness returned. She still guarded her litter ferociously, but now, in the morning, she would lurch from her bed, rush up to me, or to Tom when he came to see her, her rear waggling, lick our faces, and dart back to her bed and the litter all in one second flat, as if to say, "I can't stay long. You know how it is, I've got these pups to take care of now, but I just wanted to let you know everything's still O.K. between us.—Sorry about the dog house—" And back in her bed, she was the ferocious guardian again and would let no one near her offspring.

The offspring were hard to part with as they grew older, though by then it mattered little to Ida. One of the brown males, promising to resemble its mother, had an appealing squeal. He grew strong, healthy, alert. This was the one we decided to keep. Tom named him Tim. This was the one, in the months that followed, who all unknowingly deposed Shag from his kingdom of house and hill and meadow. This one caused his end.

*   *   *

Shag hardly noticed him during the first few months. Tim lived outside, never allowed in the house until November grew cold, and outdoors Shag ignored him. In the woods Shag and Ida ran too fast, so that Tim bounced and rolled after them, squealing just like a small boy whose elders won't wait for him.

Shag always made it home ten minutes before Tim, crawling into his favorite hiding place under the Cotoneasters, where he had dug himself a cool, damp, fragrant hole. Tim could search all day and never find him.

We were glad we had chosen Tim to keep. We said he was not too frisky to bother Shag, nor too stubborn to learn from his elders. But he was playful, scampering in the yard after a blowing leaf, riding on hind legs like a brown, bobbing, rocking horse, yapping melodiously, pretending to pounce on the vicious leaf though never quite dropping on it. The first freezing day, when he was let inside, he leapt through the doorway, missed his footing, rolled a few feet like a fat leggy barrel, righted himself, padded through the living room and bedrooms, tongue dripping. It seemed he had already gone through the house a thousand times before. It was his. He entered, possessor of all its rooms, and completed his survey of it with swift, short-legged gyrations around the edges of carpets, under chairs, into the fireplace, strewing ashes like a dervish in a windstorm. And abruptly, in the kitchen, confronted Shag in his bed.

Our quiet puppy lurched, rose to his hind legs, set up an uncouth barking, and danced and careened around Shag, and bounced against him and snapped at his paws and ears and tail. Then, nose to the delicious scents on the linoleum, swerved like lightning to Shag's water bowl and drained it.

But this was Shag's world. Shag rose in his bed, not too swiftly, stretching his small self as high as he could. He blinked and looked up to me questioningly. Then slowly he turned back to Tim and relentlessly stared, but with dignity and patience, merely waiting in his broken slumber until this disturbance should be removed. But once Tim had emptied the water bowl and sent it spinning like a top across the floor, he rolled into bed against Shag and nipped at the soft black fur of his throat, rat's-tail wagging like a wind-tossed reed, paying no heed to Shag's taut head, jerked away as he drew himself back and studied the puppy with polite, but impatient-growing, black eyes. Whereupon Tim, not knowing rebuff, bounced obliviously into the living room and the best chair. Curled up. Fell sound asleep.

Ida watched all of it with her bright, guiltless eyes. It was the weeks that followed that began the gradual undermining of Shag's ego, all that the years had given him vanishing like mist against his own desperate will. At the outset he hazarded indifference, but how be indifferent when Tim chose to lie wherever he lay, sniff where he sniffed? Even, outdoors, making friends with the loathed, stupid King? On the second evening at bedtime, Tim not only again drained and upset Shag's water bowl, but ended with dank paws and drenched belly fur in bed beside Shag. Shag twitched, rose up aloof and glowering, but Tim wound up in a ball, buried nose under paw, and fell fast asleep. So was Shag to share his couch with this thin-tailed, lop-eared pup? He waited fully five minutes, his eyes flicking in outrage about the room, but the browbeaten look, too, coming into his gaze; then himself descended from the bed with slow step. And ever after slept on the floor.

He had no weapons. Though Tim was chased out of the bed, Shag would not go back into it. He knew the time of abdication had come. For the first few days, he would leap unexpectedly into my lap (he, who with male detachment, had always scorned to be a lap dog) and once settled in that safe area, a sigh of unspeakable magnitude would escape from him. But after two or three times, he seemed to know that not even a lap was sanctuary. Not mine. Not Tom Dell's.

While Tim went his gay way. Time, we still hoped, would

bring reconciliation, or at least acceptance. But on another morning, as Tim flashed open his eyes, stretched, humped up his rear, and in that stretching absorbed again all the vitality he had spent the day before, next leaping with a glad yip from his new bed toward Shag's hard bed on the floor, Shag also leapt—had he slept at all during the night, or lain awake with his twisted thoughts?—and with a snarl of real rage and panic, bared his pitifully small fangs to the suddenly cowering Tim.

But before teeth could reach flesh, a hand, my own, ungoverned, harder than it meant, much harder, shot against Shag's ribs. He stopped, stunned, a low growl caught in his throat. But he did not move. Tom Dell looked at me as if he wished I might lose my offending hand, and I wished it, too. It went to Shag's back with murmured apologies. Even stupid Tim whimpered and licked against Shag. But Shag knew. He slunk to a corner and pressed himself out of sight against the wall.

His shame was consummate. His glance never lost its accusing hurt. He lay comatose, rising only when Tim drew near, when he sprang up and waited, trembling, until Tim wandered away. Then he panted back to the floor, neck stretched out to allow his black head to press against the wall, and never, these days, sleeping, as if always to watch out for some new terrifying shame.

Then at the end of two weeks he began to play.

With his natural dignity, he had played little even as a puppy. Now he was a desolate and senile buffoon playing tag. Tom Dell brought up a rubber mouse for the puppy. Tim coursed through the house, shaking the mouse until it seemed his own ears would shake themselves loose; dashing, halting, shaking, butting like a goat; then flinging the bedraggled mouse high upward, until he himself dropped exhausted, with mouth ecstatically laughing.

Shag watched. After a week of eating nothing (*it will pass,* the vet said, *it often happens, he'll adjust himself*) he had begun to eat voraciously, not only his own food but gobbling Tim's too when he could, and then Ida's. Where Tim was, Shag was. Then one day Tim dropped his mouse at his master's feet, waiting for it to be tossed, when with a feverish yelp Shag shot out of a corner. He caught the mouse in his teeth. He yapped and chased and darted under legs and over chairs and grew breathless far before his time and jumped against the master's stunned arms, the mouse grotesquely dangling. And all the while his eyes were begging—*Play! Play with me—see, I'll play with you too!*

The nightmarish sight lasted five minutes. He tried to toss the mouse, but fumbled and lost it, snarlingly retrieved it; all the while he waited for Tom's or my praise which never came. Even Tim watched in silence. Shag scurried with his old bones under tables and chairs until he made himself dizzy. He dropped at last at my feet. His ribs swelled and contracted, tongue lopping far out of his mouth; and as Tim came up to sniff questioningly, in Shag's eyes was the frantic, monstrous attempt at grinning as one might find in the leer of a drunken child.

Now he was lured outside into the November sunshine with the greatest difficulty. He never shed the dumb defeat. After much coaxing, he would drag himself to the door. Outside he blinked cravenly to left and right, then waddled like something half dead ten or fifteen feet around the yard. If by accident Tim got outside with Shag and pounced in play against him, he merely halted, jerked his head backward, waited for Tim to stop and go away, but no more with anger or impatience; instead, limitless resignation.

"Shag! . . . Good Shag! . . ." Not this, nor the hopeful snapping of fingers, nor conciliatory pats, could make him raise his eyes as he lay all day long in his corner. Ida came, sniffed, sat for a while beside him, then walked away. Finding himself forgotten, he seemed to forget everyone else—Tim, Ida, Tom, me. He refused food and water, and grew incredibly small.

But then on that last day, he got to his feet and began to roam from room to room, silently, though still ignoring Tom's encouraging laugh, Tim's playful yip as he rushed toward him, the mouse in his puppy teeth. Food was fixed—Shag would eat again! But he halted over the bowl of food. He stared at it for a full minute. Then he walked away.

Why did he flick his eyes about him with their curious, blank accusation and then go swiftly toward the door? He gave a faint bark and scratched against the door jamb. He was let out, lingered a moment on the terrace, looked to right and left, then made for the hills on padding, rapid feet.

It was Ida who found him, under the hazel thicket where he had sometimes liked to lie on hot days. Ida's barks brought Tim the Pretender to the thicket, to sniff with the glint of play in his puppy eyes. Tim's yips brought Tom and me (and Tom, of course, was the one who later buried him) and then even the despised King, wandering nearby, glided over on his sleek feet to see what was under the hazel thicket. Then King glided away and went to doze in the sun and Ida loped off after King and Tim wheeled after Ida to nip at her ankles; and none gave any more notice to Shag's, or Artemis Flanders', passing.

16

Pyramid Builders

THEY are the real pyramid builders. That is, field mice. They are cunning and conniving. But I feel no real anger toward them. They did much to make Jane March a part of our world.

They move into the basement each fall, though it might be better to have them inside than out, where they make nests in the marsh hay covering on the garden and gnaw away at the daphnes underneath, or dig their spectacular labyrinthine tunnels under the snow and all unknown to you chew enjoyably away at the trunks of the crabapple or beach-plum trees.

But inside, their cunning only increases—the gray shadow flitting from the air draft along the baseboard to vanish under a chest of drawers before you know what you've seen. Trapped, as they sometimes are by falling into a laundry tub or pail, they are engaging to watch, once their panic subsides. They wash their faces like cats, and feed on their hind legs like chipmunks, forepaws held up to their busy mouths. Their faint, pure squeal is not unmusical. But these are rodents that live by their wits,

and it's their wits that cause the trouble. You give them poisoned wheat and they scornfully peel off the tainted outer shell, eat the sweet healthy kernel, and leave the husks behind in a neat pyramidal pile for you to clean up.

They outwitted Jane March about the sweet corn. It's true that corn, picked from a garden at sundown and rushed to a pot of boiling water, is another vegetable from that which one finds in city markets. This difference alone may have made Jane begin to love the country. Corn, freshly picked (and the picking itself is an important part—the soft dust underfoot, the dry fragrance blowing through the tall stalks, the rustle of the growing leaves), has milk in its kernels as sweet as new wine. Corn season at Jane's house now is a time of boiled or steamed corn, morning, noon, and night, or roasted corn, or fresh corn soup, or fritters, or soufflé. The season ends in a triumph of corn relish, made from all the corn she and her friends haven't been able to eat. She eats corn like a pig. She gets fat on it, too, and has to spend October restricted to rye crisp and remorse.

It had become a pleasant, familiar sight to see Jane moving about Paulie's house, watering Paulie's trees, or sitting in the porch swing on late afternoons reading Paulie's books—it was good, because you knew that gradually, yet surely, the land was laying its touch on her. You saw it in her eyes, as she put down her book, to gaze off over the shadowy hills toward the Littens' house. You saw it in the color returning to her cheeks. You heard it in her voice, growing clear, like the song of wind over the marshes.

It had begun that night I took her to Aunt Dell's for supper, and invited Bud Devere along. She was overwhelmed at the outset by the enormous, elastic family Aunt Dell seemed to have, crowded around the table. She was miffed by Buss, the vandalic one, who appeared at table three times and ate three meals. Aunt Dell huffed and piled a dinner fit for Thanksgiving on the white-clothed table.

"Look, it ain't much, ainna? Just a little supper," she cried woefully. "She don't eat nothing—she don't like the supper?" She kept speaking of Jane as an absent, third person.

Flecks of laughter began in Jane's eyes. Soon she ate quite lustily. I smiled at Jane. Aunt Dell had triumphed. Bud Devere, too, watched her thoughtfully.

Before the evening ended, with ice cream on Aunt Dell's front porch, Bud had offered to work the Waldeen farm for her.

Aunt Dell sighed, sniffing enjoyable turmoil, and put her big hand over Jane's. "It's give plenty the neighbors to talk about, ainna?" She sighed again, more hugely, but then flashed her smile. "Him so young. You so young. Ainna?"

Jane said to hell with that, smiled pleasantly—I was surprised at her language, though Aunt Dell seemed to glow—and said that if Bud would be such a good guy as to work the farm, she'd share profits with him and not bother about neighbors' gossip. Anyway, she wanted to keep the farm going, in case Ed Waldeen should ever come back after his lonely hegira to the city.

Aunt Dell and Jane became friends. Aunt Dell had a mist in her blue eyes as we left—she had taken a new soul to her capacious, golden bosom. The first opportunity that presented itself, at Ladies' Aid Meeting, she began a campaign for Jane, even though Jane herself was not yet ready for it, that ended with Jane being picked to be the girl who falls into a vat of water when you trip a target with a fast-slung soft ball at our Firemen's Picnic. It's a high honor in our village

Jane said she wouldn't go. It was ridiculous. Oh, Jane, please, don't be angry inside, let us in. . . . She read my thoughts.

"All right," she said quietly. "I'll be the fall girl." Then she was suddenly laughing.

She made more money at the picnic than any other girl had in recent years, so the women didn't mind their men spending their money on her. Her widowhood, slowly, was dropping from her. Too, her strangeness. Everyone was willing, now, to become her neighbor—when she was ready.

She was finally ready, I think, the wintry night we went down to John Hummock's house. Jane had tried growing corn her first summer out here. It had not even tasseled. And John Hummock's corn was a sore spot with many of us, because his always ripened a full three weeks before any of ours. May nights are likely to etch themselves in unexpected frost, so you don't dare plant corn until June. So August is the season of ripe corn. But John's always tassel proudly, then burst into milky ripeness by mid-July.

Jane's passion made her determined to have the earliest corn in the county that next year. I went to the Hummocks' with her. She was armed with wine for John, some old copies of women's magazines for Edna Hummock, for which Edna thanked her coolly, saying she had her own subscriptions.

But she did invite us to stay and watch television. Five Hummock children crawled over Jane while she watched. I could see her gradually relax, in the spotless, though not very cheerful, farm kitchen. She rumpled the kids' hair, retied their bows. The Hummocks have television—not a table model either, but an expensive set—but no plumbing, and later when Jane had to go to the outhouse Mrs. Hummock sent the children along, since it was near their bedtime.

They all went, waiting their turns in a neat line outside in the black, gusty, end-of-winter night, and two of the smallest, a boy and girl, went inside with Jane because they were afraid of the dark. It made Jane feel exactly like a country schoolteacher, she said later, responsible for her charges, looking out for their needs and watching over them in the inclement weather.

When she returned inside, she was glowing. The Hummocks seemed to know how good it made her feel, because Mrs. Hummock got out some thick steaks and fried them, along with a pan of potatoes, for a bedtime snack, and John, grinning, broke down and told about his early corn.

He was lifting frozen sod from the pasture in early April, cutting it in chunks, starting the seeds in the overturned chunks in a cold frame, then merely transplanting chunks and all in the field rows when the time was safe, and gaining a three or four weeks' head start.

Jane thanked him heartily.

John said, "Oh, nuts, Mrs. March, good luck." He looked embarrassed.

On the way home, I noticed Jane's silence. "It was nice of John to give away his secret to you, wasn't it?" I asked.

Her voice was small. "Yes."

*   *   *

She sent to a New York seed grower for the fanciest, most expensive hybrid corns (still with the city idea that it would grow and taste better because it cost more, though she could get state-tested hybrid seed right at our own mill)—midget, Purple Cross, which is a revolting corn to look at, its rows of kernels stained a sickly purple, but tastes fine, and the earliest, pearliest whites, and the fattest bantams. She put Bud to work building a cold frame. She talked me into cutting sod from the field in a freezing drizzle, and hauling it into her basement. Each of the chunks of sod got its nugget of seed one evening, and next morning she would move them outside to the new cold frame. It seemed a kind of rite, a time of jubilation, high with expectation, and we sat in her parlor afterward, drinking highballs, Jane, Bud, and myself.

We sat around the fire, telling Jane stories about Paulie and Ed, and their last party in this house. Jane listened carefully, her trim legs crossed, her hands quiet in her lap. But while we were talking, the mice were busy in the cellar. By next morning each of the chunks of sod had a neat pile of dirt beside it, and every kernel had been adroitly lifted from every chunk. Every mouse in the basement, and there must surely have been dozens, all scurrying and digging and squealing to call more mice, had feasted on hybrid corn that night. I was surprised to know it wasn't too annoying to Jane, since even mice, like men, she said, must eat; they are, after all, free souls. It was good to see Jane accepting country ways, though they were only the ways of mice, and Bud and I dug more sod that afternoon and Jane replanted the chunks, this time with local corn. Together we lugged them out to the cold frame before a mouse could so much as whet its claws.

But that same day she planted up some pots with fancy seeds of West Indian gherkins and Special Fordhook pickling cucumbers, these destined for her summer's dill crock, into whose wonder and mystery Aunt Dell had already initiated her. She planted only a few seeds from each packet, and left the packets next to the pots. Again she forgot the pots in the basement overnight, while we went over to Genesee dancing, along with Bud and his girl. When she remembered next morning and went down to rescue them, she was ready not to be astonished to find the seeds dug up again.

But mice plan their surprises subtly. The pots were intact, except one. Not a grain of earth had been lifted from them, not a seed. Instead, the mice had walked off with the seeds she hadn't planted, packages and all, only mice know where. There wasn't a shred of chewed paper around or any seed husks in one of these everpresent neat piles they have such a mania for building.

It made her break out laughing—such complete disappearance. How many mice does it take to carry a heavy packet of seeds? Then she noticed the one pot they had disturbed. All the ground had been emptied out, and in its bottom lay six brand-new mice on a nest of cotton wisps. And then, a foot away, she saw the mother mouse, upright, placidly watching her, alertly interested, as if she were waiting to hear what Jane would say about her litter. It was nearly a minute before the mouse came to with a squeal, raced to nip at Jane's finger, and went tearing off.

For an instant there though, Jane said, it seemed all the world was friends.

But at least they had been remarkably neat about carrying the seed packages away with them, and piling up the dirt from the pot. Their passion for arranging their debris in trim conical mounds is impressive. They have the instincts of the ancient pyramid builders coupled with a German housewife's compulsion to tidiness.

I had learned of this habit the winter before, Jane's first winter out here, when it became necessary for me to make another trip to New York. But this was to be a pleasant journey, only a matter of one or two weeks, no fears, no nothing, except a placid contentment—it was to be only a short trip on business about the motion picture. It remained exactly that, a brief, enjoyable venture into a strange big city for which I no longer felt much of anything. When I left for home again, it was not even with relief. I simply was going home, where I belonged.

Before I had left, a friend in Alabama had sent up a huge sack of peanuts, no less than a bushelful, from his garden. It was a lot of peanuts to eat, even with the help of Tom and Buss Dell and their friends in the village. When I left, at least half of the peanuts still were on hand, stored in the flour bin in the kitchen.

I came back home one snowy day, stopped in the village for supplies and talked a while with Gus, a man of small horizons who helps out in the store.

"Where you been? Haven't seen you around much lately."

"I spent a while in New York."

"Oh?"

"Yes."

"How the roads out that way?"

"Fine."

"Much snow?"

"Nope."

"Oh."

The subject of travel exhausted, supplies stacked in the car, I started home, my heart beating as it always does when I've been away, ever mindful of how dangerously near I had come to not letting this be my home. I honked as I passed Aunt Dell's to let her know I was back (wherever she is, she hears the honk and can recognize people by their honks as others recognize the human voice) and started up the hill to the house.

You move to the country, become part of it, and whenever you leave your house you return to it with a vague apprehension that in your absence it may simply have vanished. Houses have been known to disappear overnight around here in the owner's absence, as if blown away by a demon wind, leaving no trace, as Llewellyn's house did. Late at night, with the countryside asleep and especially on hidden back roads, there is no one to see the clarion signs in the sky of an empty house that has burst into flames. Or to hear the hammering that must mean a man's house was being dismantled, shingle by shingle, beam by beam, detached from the earth on which it rested, and simply scooted away, the way it happened to unlucky Llewellyn as recently as fifty years ago.

It is a favorite hilarious story of Walter Cwym's to tell over in Genesee, sitting around his kitchen table and drinking his applejack, which has a translucent honey color and a fragrance, hidden beneath its alcoholic power, of a hundred acres of apple trees staggering with ripe fruit, but this fragrance blown to one from miles away, so that only a dim trace reaches the nostrils.

Llewellyn, who came to the county near the turn of the century, was a bachelor, a drunkard, unwelcome, not giving a hoot.

He was unwelcome because of his drunkenness, which to many Welshmen is the one sin for which there is no forgiveness. It was doubly grievous to his brothers, as well as to God, because he was a Welshman himself, and so shamed his own people. But he also had hermit ways. Untroubled, he built himself a shack of logs, collected a table, chair, pots, mattress, and settled himself to a lazy, fumey, slovenly life among his neighbors. Even a visit from the church elders couldn't dislodge him, or next, their direct threats. The Welsh are a silent race, except when they sing, and then it is not their lips speaking but their hearts. Toward Llewellyn they grew utterly silent, as if he didn't exist, and shifted their strategy to one of waiting. Late in fall Llewellyn hitched up for a five or six-day trip into the city thirty miles away by horse and wagon (one day in, one day back, the rest for carousing) to bring home his winter supplies, since not even the storekeeper of his village would sell him so much as a rind of bacon. After six days, he came home. His house was gone. There was a pond where his house had been. The pond still exists, and I first learned about Llewellyn's story one cool spring, when walking over a neighbor's farm, and we came upon a lapping, icy pool, and hurried up to it to see whether any frogs had yet begun their public mating along its green-gray, cluttered fringe, and the farmer with me muttered, with a hoarse, secret laugh, *Be careful, you'll fall in Llewellyn's house!* No one calls it a pond. It's always called Llewellyn's house.

His neighbors had given him what they thought he deserved, and without so much as a murmur of recrimination or further argument. They just did it. While he was off in town carousing, they banded together, dismantled his house log by log, carted away his furniture, removed even his outhouse, dug out a bush or two he had planted to gaze on in his balmy solitude, found a spring nearby, dug it deep and flooded the hollow where his house had been into the pond that still bubbles and stretches and today harbors bass and blue gills. (So that you wonder, where did those first fish come from, and how did nature mysteriously plant them in a pond with neither outlet nor inlet other than the spring?) When Llewellyn came home, every one of his neighbors faced him blankly, as they would a stranger. They regarded him with polite curiosity, a man they had never seen before. They pondered, searched their memories, but then told him that even his name was unfamiliar to them. What had he said his name was? Llewellyn, he cried. Llewellyn who? I'm Llewellyn Draves! The men shook their heads, and looked at each other mutely.

It was like walking into a world that had simply disappeared. One or two dour-faced neighbors even walked over his former fields to stare along with him, but not with the incredible wonder that was in his groggy eyes, at the leaf-strewn pond that glistened where Llewellyn dazedly kept insisting his house had been.

Until finally he climbed back into his wagon and drove away forever, no doubt a shaken man.

*　　*　　*

But unlike Llewellyn's, the house looked safe as I came up the drive that wintry day. It looked cold, forlorn, but comfortable. The beaten regular paths of cottontails in the snow encircled it, like avenues of a thickly populated city, and the delicate, light tracks of squirrels, and a few human gashes of a solitary hunter.

It is pleasant to unlock the doors, feel the winter's damp chill rush at you as if in a hurry to get outside and out of your way, now that you're back; and you carry in luggage and supplies and start a woodfire until the furnace warms the house, and you wander from room to room and there is the intense expectant pleasure of beginning something over again, of re-establishing a warm, sensible continuity that had been roughly broken. You can sit all night staring into the fire, thankful that you're back and have no place you need to go.

Then you unpack the groceries, while the security keeps growing inside you, despite the snow falling outdoors. You check the phone to see if it still works, hear the operator's same voice with surprise, as if you hadn't expected to find her still there, same earphones to her ears, plugging in the same misconnecnections, all this while you've been gone.

It's best to come home alone, because then you sense more acutely that this is where you belong; all this is yours alone. Even so, you glance through the window over the dimming, white twilit fields toward the Waldeens' house, where Jane March is living now, and you begin thinking, as I did that evening, how nice if she lived here, too, were sharing this homecoming with you. If only she could find the same peace you have found. . . .

Then it's also good to phone a few friends—Aunt Dell, John Hummock, Bud—just to make sure nothing has changed while you were gone. There has been no Llewellyn's house of the spirit, either. Aunt Dell shouts a huge, waltzlike welcome. John Hummock is sober, blunt, and cordial. Bud curses. He says, Well you god-damned fool so you're back, how was it?

You're back.

I went to stash away onions and potatoes in the flour bin, and caught sight of the big sack in which the peanuts had been left. It was collapsed and empty. It must have been mice. The winter was long and cold. Mice get hungry. With spring so near, the mice would soon leave the cellar and return to the fields, and if I had helped nourish them for a few weeks during the long sleepy winter, it made me feel only neighborly. And their thoroughness was gratifying, because not so much as a peanut shuck was left in the bag, nor any mess left on the flour-bin floor. Very tidy, I thought, with a strange comfortableness. And then there were bags to unpack, and suits to hang up in the closet.

From the flour bin in the kitchen to the clothes closet in the bedroom is a good distance. The flour bin is at the far end of the kitchen, and the closet at the far end of the bedroom, and you must walk through a hall and the long living room to get from one to the other. But in the closet, every shoe, every slipper, work boot, mukluk, was filled to overflowing with peanut shucks piled in cone-shaped mounds. With scrupulous neatness, too. Not a dry musty shell had been dropped to the floor.

It was hard not to admire those mice for their ingenuity, or feel fond toward them for their industry and consideration, though it may only have been dumb instinct. When I went to bed, I was still pleasantly computing the number of mice-miles they must have traveled during the winter, carrying each shuck from bin to closet, and then back to the bin for more shucks.

You feel a wonderful exhaustion on a first night home from a trip. The bed, your own bed, looks fresh and soft as you jump in and the sheets promise a cold enjoyable shock—as I expected; I jumped right out again. As anyone would who had flung himself on a compact layer, between the undersheet and the mattress, of more crackling, stabbing peanut shells.

You feel a sudden affection for owls, who eat mice.

*   *   *

Jane became a birdwatcher. It was exciting to see her finally fall in love with earth and sky, the life of both, exactly as I had done, hovering for a while between two worlds, finally exchanging them, learning to find the utmost reality in a leaf, or hill, or lark's song.

Her special fascination was for big birds—the pagan hunting owl in his slow, heavy flight, searching for mice, lemmings, snakes, even for smaller owls, rabbits, or weasels. Or the ghostly snowy owl.

Its beauty was so unexpected as to make its existence seem implausible and otherworldly. Other needs had risen in Jane since she came to the country. Her widowhood, and trying to understand her husband Skip's death, and then a growing gratitude for what was happening to her, made her look in churches.

She would drag me, and sometimes Bud, along, all of us feeling clean and neat and healthy on Sunday mornings, standing around in the sunshine talking with neighbors afterward, sometimes inviting them or being invited by them to Sunday dinner; or stamping snow from our feet in the small, ill-lighted vestibule on Wednesday nights during Advent or Lent, seeing all the ruddy, patient faces in the pews.

You go to a country church and the gilt and fading blue angels around the altar are badly, naïvely, often grotesquely painted, but this is all right, for they have tried, the angels have honestly striven to soar on their flaking wings and the peeling saints are earnestly saintly. They seem more devout than the garish saints of bigger, more expensive, city churches. Perhaps we didn't listen much to the sermons; and the choir singing may have been more ardent than musical. But the feeling was right.

It felt like church, a place to consider and search and accept. The congregation looks real and plain as the earth itself. On summer Sunday mornings you see the clean authoritative sun through the windows. There isn't much stained glass in country churches. The people in the pews open their purses cautiously, lose their places in songbooks, cough through the long sermon, pretending to listen raptly. There is a sudden, enormous devotion. And why am I always so moved to find our corner bartender there, a big, quiet man who has recently married a pretty, talkative widow? Sitting in a disorderly row with him (while she is home cooking Sunday dinner) are her eight children. He doesn't look comfortable in a church, too big, awkward, beery-breathed, but respectful. But he has accepted the eight squirming children. He looks like a man of his word.

Driving home from a Wednesday evening service, we saw the snowy owl. From a fencepost along a buried, stripped cornfield, the round head shone in a momentary flash of the headlights before the lights roused him. He gave a shaking croak, then a piercing whistle, before he ascended in ponderous, jerky flight. It is always these big birds in motion that seem so outlandishly breath-taking, as this one did as he flew away like a spectral frozen cloud, a ghost of other great birds, of a shadowy purity. Though his feathers were barred in brown, this tinge of color vanished in motion and all one saw was a rushing, moonlit ball of white that should have been ungainly but flew like flight itself. And why did I feel such ineffable warmth and completeness as Jane gripped my arm?

In spring you get up before dawn to walk with Jane, with binoculars, sandwiches, a thermos of coffee, to hunt for more outsize birds, the wild swans and geese that rest during their migration on the marshes a few miles west of here. These are broad marshes, covering mile after mile, and they are desolate and drear, overhung with a miasma of doom as marshes should be. Canadian geese, hulking white swans, settle here for a while on their way north, and swoop down to the somber water not by the dozen or the hundred, but in clouds of thousands, enough to make a separate nation of birds. Seeing their descent, their brief visit, their artful feeding, hearing their shrieks, is a moment of clear annunciation. It is spring again and the restlessness in the marshes and through the hardwoods and on the fields has begun, and the same great, seething restlessness fills even the cold air. You believe in something again, and deny catastrophe.

But one big solitary bird can be as arresting as thousands. It was the second winter Jane lived out here, and the December snowfalls had made the hills twice as high, and the picnic tables outside became sarcophagi hiding unknown bodies inside snowy shrouds, and the fields were alive with miniature plants and trees and ferns of glittering snow-crystal as it hung on dried weeds. Jane was in her yard, her hair blowing, snow fringeing her lashes, biting her cheeks and chin raw, and was splitting logs expertly for a woman, especially one who such a brief while ago had not loved the country.

I watched for a while. "Not like having cocktails at the Pump Room."

"Hell, no," Jane said.

"Wish you were there?"

"Sometimes. Not now."

"Want to go for a walk?"

"Sure."

"Jane—do you feel you belong here now?"

She was momentarily thoughtful. But her smile broke slowly. "Yes." She turned from me, going toward the shed.

She stood the ax inside the shed, gave her hair a shake to let out a shower of ice crystals, and looked reflectively at the ax.

"Beautiful instrument, isn't it?" she said.

"Sure is."

"Sure is," she repeated. "Wish I could think as clean as this cuts."

"My grandfather used to say, keep using it every day, you will."

"I don't doubt it." She laughed in a kind of awe. She was flushed with hard work and accomplishment. "Where do you want to walk to?"

"Why not your own woods?"

"That's where I want, but sometimes it makes me feel braggy to suggest it. Like I'm showing off. I still can't get used to it—owning a woods like that. It almost doesn't make sense. In a way, it scares you. Seems piggish."

I knew what she meant. Behind her place is a woods but it is not like other woods—it is a conifer forest, thirty evergreen acres planted years ago by Ed Waldeen's father, a devoted conservationist, proof of one man's love for the world, the planting grown now into a dense stand of spruces, European and American larches, Scotch pines, white and red pines, red cedars and hemlocks and tamaracks. When seen with snow on every needle of every branch while one walks through the tunnels of outspreading arms and glances up to its high white steeples almost out of sight, a known world vanishes and a new but ancient, everlasting world comes to replace it, though a tenth of a mile away runs the loud highway.

There, that day, we found the Reeves pheasant, quite tame, undisturbed by us, strutting a half-dozen yards away through the red and mossy-green and shaggy, pinkish tree trunks. Jane found its trail first, the rhythmic imprint of its claws, and always to one side the thin vein left in the snow by its dragging plume.

We did not expect to see the bird itself but there he was, bright in colors like any other pheasant, but astonishing for his tail fully four feet long. He moved in slow splendor on his pavement of snow, and first his body would move by to be seen behind the openings in the ground-grazing branches, but then, body vanished, the tail appeared, like the longest and courtliest train, and it seemed five minutes before the tail had dragged by, drawn in such unconscious pride over the white earth. Then Jane gave a small cry.

The bird had risen in flight. It raised itself casually, in a slow, whirring motion, its tail spinning round and round like a gyroscope, or propeller, neither bird nor feather ever touching one of the dense lacinated branches; and Jane whispered that the bird was guided this way through the sparse, clear channels among the branches by some subtle interplay of air pressure. The long spinning bright tail at last disappeared like an hallucination against the snow-heavy sky.

"Oh look, Jane—there he goes!"

"Look!" she answered.

"I am—yes, look! Jane, will you marry me?"

"Yes, I'd love to—but look at him soar!"

"I see him! When?"

"Give me a few more months, will you? Look at him—do you see him?"

"Yes, I see him—!"

"Yes, yes, for God's sake, look!"

Then Jane was exultantly laughing, her eyes shining clear. These were cries of wonder at love and the universe, the best cries men can make.

17

Anniversary

BUT before the hills and sky and air had taught Jane and me what we could give each other, there were other moments that need telling. There was the sad sound of Paulie's song coming to a close, before Jane had even moved here. . . .

There was the day, too, when Miss Millie, sly, kind, wise Millie Litten, was gone. That was the news I heard one day as summer drew to a close. Millie—irretrievably gone.

Nearby is a forgotten cemetery, where I thought she must be lying when I first heard the news. It lies within thirty feet of a new superhighway that was recently built, and Buck Fife's brother-in-law, who worked on the road crew, discovered this forgotten place one hot afternoon when he went to rest in the high grasses alongside the road shoulder after the sun had nearly knocked him out. It is really a forgotten graveyard. Later, his zeal fired, as the most unsuspecting man can be fired to peculiar passions he doesn't dream are in him, he went on his Saturday off to search the records at the county office. But he could find no mention of this plot, though years ago the WPA had mapped all old cemeteries in the county. He was even told by a laconic and obstinate clerk that no such plot existed.

But it does. Sig Fife had seen it with his own eyes. He took me there. It is a disturbing corner of oblivion, for it lies in such disrepair, lilac roots crawling and clutching at fallen stones and the thick lilac branches trying to hide what its roots cannot reach. It is as if nature were trying first to crumble the evidence and then send up a screen to hide man's neglect of his brothers —for this half acre is so fraught with his almost palpable forgetfulness, his unconcern for past and finished loves. It is a severance of time, a discontinuance of a stream of life. Here lie a handful of remnants without past or future, a cluster of men and their wives and children and parents, forgotten, fallen into anonymity, like a lost race, for even the names still discernible on the stones are unknown around here now. No one preserves these people by even a faint, anecdotal memory, as though a whole era of history had dropped into the ground and was covered by weeds and saplings growing strong to crack the stones and further obliterate the memory of them, and by sheltering thickets of hazelnut and insidious, warning arms of poison ivy.

These people must still exist somewhere in old photograph albums. But whatever their existence meant, in our earliest days of statehood, is unrecorded now and unhonored. So as one wanders among the stones and squints to read off the names and dates, a host of stories invent themselves, creation rising from decay.

It is astonishing that, nearly a hundred years ago, so many died so young. Only one man of reasonable age is buried there —but who was Persis Carlton, of Concord, Massachusetts? What was this New Englander doing here among the Welsh, Scandinavians, and Germans, dying at the age of seventy in

1852, but leaving no descendants to mark other stones (or tend his grave)? You know why there are so many graves of newborn children, but why did so many adults die so young, men and women in their twenties, thirties, or at most, inexorably in their forties? A sudden blast of cool wind reminds you of the desolate winters out here. Perhaps the wind is answering. But many of these deaths occurred in summer—July, August. Plague, dysentery? But no one summer took any greater toll than any other.

What of this chiseled pair of clasped hands? Mother and child, the mother dying at thirty-one on a dreary third of April in 1850. But the baby died on July eighteenth of that same year, at the age of three months and fifteen days. So the mother died in childbirth, but the child survived for three months longer —but who took care of the child then, and what of the husband, whose name is on none of the stones? Did he wander away to newer land?

What of the Capen brothers? Three boys lost in a single year, boys of twenty, twenty-one, twenty-three, in the strength of youth. But then you read the year of death: 1864. Three soldiers. But how were they brought north for burial, or does this tall, soft-stoned obelisk mark empty graves?

And what of Mr. Earnest Shipstead? His stone was successfully concealed by nature, not only entangled with lilac roots but overlaid with creeping sod. A flat slab, its marble surface chiseled with a mournful willow, name, date of death. Earnest Shipstead: age fifteen years, plus some months, plus days. But then read the inscription. *Remember all ye who pass me by, And shed a tear, For a loving husband And father of six lies here.*

Earnest he was! You reflect that those were days of splendor, of bold, proud, strutting men who made our nation, fathering in youth and abundantly. But nature makes jokes. Unhappily, a three-day rain and the following burst of sunshine wash and cleanse and bleach the stone and restore a thinly etched line to the slab, adding a stroke to a digit, so that the prodigious father becomes a dull and normal forty-five. But Sig Fife and I still have a tender feeling for Earnest. For a few weeks, unknown to him among all these other unknowns, he was close to glory.

*   *   *

In my mind I saw Millie put here to rest, and when I think of it now inscriptions still carve themselves out, plain as from a stonecutter's hand. Gone, lost, torn from us. Nevermore to return. Alas, how we shall miss thee. How we shall never see thy bright small face again. Alas, Miss Millie. Gone. Here lies a good, great woman.

It wasn't precisely that kind of absence, however. But that kind of grief did fill the air for the first few instants the day Carrie telephoned to say Millie was gone. It was the tone of her voice that seeded the thought—low, vague, beaten. "Hi," she said, "I thought you might come over and have supper with me. Could you?" An uncertainty came into her voice as she added—"alone."

"I always come alone, don't I?"

"Me. I'm alone," she said, with a shy laugh. Then the thunder-news. "Mildred's gone." Mildred, instead of Millie, made it formal and ghastly.

"Oh? Shopping?"

There was a silence before Carrie said, "No. I mean, she's gone."

It was the way her voice faded that made the heart sink. "Oh, no!"

There was complete silence now, so I suppose Carrie was nodding at the other end of the line.

"You don't mean really gone, Miss Carrie?" I asked. "Would you like me to rush over? Are you all right?"

"She's gone off on her wedding trip."

Millie is at least in her late sixties. I laughed, I suppose, in relief. "What's the joke? You mean Millie's got herself a boy friend?" But continued silence, an angry void at the other end (Millie and Carrie rarely use the telephone for much reciprocal conversation; it is largely a listening device for them) made the truth of Carrie's announcement suddenly clear. I strained my mind for prospects. "What do you mean, she's really gone off? With who?"

"Whom," Carrie said, who had once been a schoolteacher.

"All right. With whom?"

But no answer, and a finality in that reluctance to communicate that made it seem grief had finally overwhelmed her, and she must have fallen to the floor in a faint.

It made me hurry as fast as a whole flock of administering angels to her side. Any one of Carrie's and Millie's neighbors would do much for them, but when one is shorn of the other he would do double of anything. The first thing I saw was the old upright piano in their parlor, and the full gloom of Millie's elopement struck me. I had picked up a sheet of music with Carrie's name written on it one time, and saw the fingering penciled in above the notes to help her practice. It said 1, 3, 5, and then 1, 2, 4, and then 2, 5, 6. The 6 was repeated often. "We play together four-handed," Carrie explained, logically enough. They play duets; they don't use duet music, but solo arrangements, and the 6 is where Millie comes in. She plays all the sharps and flats. It sounds good.

But now in my mind I could see the vacant space beside

Carrie on the piano bench. Carrie, though, hardly noticed my fallen face and led me on into the kitchen.

"Married Tom Annesley," she said and went about, quite calmly I thought, setting the table for supper. Her added bits of information fell from her lips as innocently as acorns falling from an oak tree, all unawares of the tumultuous oaks into which they would grow. "Nice boy." She took down the spoon-holder. "Very nice. I like him. You would too. Everyone does." She took two spoons out of the cutlery drawer and put them in the spoonholder, carried the holder to the table, put the spoons beside our plates, and carried the spoonholder back to the cup-board. She has an orderly mind. "Twenty-two." A cry must have escaped me, because she looked sharply at me, spots of red on her plump, cracked cheeks. "Since when isn't twenty-two old enough for a boy to be married?"

"I wasn't thinking so much of *his* age."

Carrie set to fussing around the stove, but I could see her brown hands much too busy, and a tightening around her eyes as though to defeat them in whatever their pale blue, blinking intentions might be. She shook a frying pan and beat a spoon around in a kettle quickly and popped on, and popped off and then on again, and then forgetfully once more popped off, the gas under the coffee pot. An invisible web of gas spewed out of the burner and, when I went over to push the self-lighter and save us both from being blown to pieces, she did not even notice what I did. I began to worry about her, living there alone.

"I'm happy for Mildred," she said, and sounded almost angry about it. "Tom's a hard worker. He's a good boy and no one around here's got a livelier horse or shinier buggy."

Her kitchen looked so big, with her alone in it, and though a short while ago she had finished laying the table, now she began methodically to carry all the dishes back to the cupboard. She was getting the spoonholder out again, to carry the spoons back to the drawer.

"Better leave the dishes on the table, Miss Carrie," I said, surprised at the hollow gentleness of my own voice in the expanded kitchen. "We haven't eaten supper yet. Buggy? Horse and buggy?"

She ignored it. But it seemed a reasonable enough vehicle for Millie's journey into the strange, aromatic, twilit land marriage would certainly be for her. I couldn't take my eyes off Carrie. Millie and she separated was a gross perversion of nature's plans. My eyes stung at the thought of it. Her befuddlement wasn't even funny now, it was nothing she herself could chuckle at, as she sometimes did when she caught herself doing things backward. She and Millie couldn't even get dressed properly without each other's clothes to put on. Mrs. Fife told me how at one Fish and Game Commission meeting at Moriah School (they are ardent preservers and turn in at least a dozen out-of-season hunters every year, and never fail to try to collect a bounty on them), one pair of their overshoes got lost and so each went home wearing one boot of the remaining pair. They put their arms around each other, tucked up their bootless feet, and hopped through the slush out to the Essex on the two booted feet. Seemed natural, Mrs. Fife said.

"What are you going to do now, Miss Carrie?" I asked suddenly. More questions came from me. "Where did they go on their trip? This must have happened unexpectedly, didn't it? You'd think people would have heard about it."

"Enough did," Carrie said quietly—in bitter quiet, I thought. Bud Devere and I had been up north on a fishing trip and our absence must have been the seed of my ignorance. But Carrie was going on into the parlor. She went to a card table covered with a floor-length embroidered cloth of heavy black stuff, a garland of moss roses and violets and fernery stitched heavily all around it. I had noticed the heaped table as I came in earlier. On the table rested a strange assortment. Carrie fingered them, musing to herself, and then smiled with astonishing relish. "Nice?"

"Wedding gifts?"

She nodded.

"The cloth, too? It's a beauty."

She shook her head. "Ma made it for us girls. Been stored away in a chest and Ma's law was neither one of us girls couldn't have it until it was our wedding day. And the first wed, got it. Wonder if that's what made Mildred do it."

The cloth gave off a pleasant odor of long waiting and disuse. Resting on it was a peculiar conglomeration of gifts. A decorated porcelain clock, a pair of pink-glass kerosene lamps, some fruit bowls, and a pair of long lace mitts.

"Crocheted the mitts myself," Carrie said. "Think they're too stylish for Mildred?"

Mildred, Mildred, Mildred again, I thought. Already separation and wretchedness had made her revert to the formal Christian name of baptismal scrolls and marriage certificates and writs of divorce and tombstone engravings. I searched around the room, as if somewhere I could find an answer of what to do for Carrie. I may have thought of inviting her home with me—to claim one of the acres I was saving for friends and their autumnal days. Carrie was way beyond autumn; here was the dismal, blinding paralysis of midwinter. All at once there was a terrible need to hurry, to find something to do for Carrie so that she need not be alone in this dead house for another hour. I could phone Aunt Dell, or Mrs. Fife. Except, just then, my scanning eyes went through the window and saw Miss

Millie, a small suitcase in her hand, trudging up the dusty drive.

"Here's Millie come back. Alone!" I cried.

Carrie glanced matter-of-factly toward the heaped table and the porcelain clock, which wasn't running. "She's late."

But I had also seen her glance at a streak of waning sunlight running across the carpet, reading that thin sickly finger as she might the shadow on a sundial.

I hurried out to grab the suitcase from Millie's frail hand, but also glancing at her face, trying to read there some legend of Time and its passage as Carrie had read it on the carpet. Something forbade me to ask where Tom Annesley was. But nothing else was on Millie's face, save a thin film of dust, an abundance of hard-won lines and wrinkles, a wisp of hot hair looping across her forehead, and a tired smile on her lips.

From the porch behind me Carrie asked calmly, "How was it?"

"Same as last year," Millie said, passing by me.

"You're back!" I said, with the sensation of shouting it to no one.

I followed her to the porch with the shockingly light suitcase and Carrie gave me a cool look. "Why shouldn't she be?"

I was laughing. "I don't know. Why shouldn't she be?" We could all have an unexpected party now. "But the wedding trip—"

"Always comes back every year, doesn't she?" Carrie said.

"Sure. I suppose Millie has a wedding every year, too," I said, feeling wonderful.

"Oh, *that*," Carrie said, opening the screen door. She took the suitcase from my hand and put it on the shelf of the kitchen closet without unpacking it or looking inside it. "The wedding was back in 1902."

"Or almost was," Millie said.

"But Ma dead and all, and we keeping house together, and who'd get the cloth? Didn't seem right for one of us *not* to have that embroidery."

Ma knew what she was doing, I thought.

"So I left that boy standing at the altar," Millie murmured from the rocker, while she rubbed her feet. "Today's the anniversary."

Carrie tried hard to conceal it, but there was a new springiness in her step as she went into the parlor to begin putting the wedding presents back into their cardboard carton. "Each year Millie goes on her wedding trip anyway. Takes a bus to some town and looks around, to see how it feels and make sure she didn't make any mistake," she said, low enough for only me to hear. And then called sharply out to the kitchen, "Sure it *was* all right?"

"Dirty," Millie answered. "Smoke and rubbish."

Carrie looked relieved. I think she still worries about it a little, fearing she's robbed Millie of something, or that in some dim vacant moments Millie regrets it. She had the box half-packed again, shrouding the porcelain clock in its grayed tissue paper, when she looked at me with an unexpected appeal in her blue eyes. "Don't think we ought to return these presents, do you?"

I shook my head. "I'd like to add a big bottle of champagne. Vintage 1902."

She looked at me sharply and blushed and sighed.

* * *

I stayed for supper, though I was no longer needed, and the reunion that should have been so convivial and festive instead grew reflective. Carrie must have been really shattered by the day's events, in her spaceless, timeless way, and I suppose every eighteenth day of September of every year this same, ineluctable turmoil of doubt and guilt grips her old body. Relief that Millie was safely back home only made Carrie look older during supper, the plumpness of her face falling into gentle sags of hidden, omnipresent fear, her features drained of everything but mild, exhausting thanksgiving. There was something in her silence that had been in Millie's one windy night, when we watched Carrie circling alone around the Five Points.

After supper, when dishes were done, we sat on their porch. The twilight, for a while, took on an Indian summer quality, not turning so chill as we imagined it would. Somehow, for a space, the earth did not cool. But then, somehow, it did. The new moon hung white in the blue-lit sky. They asked for their sweaters and I went in and got them. Still, the descending cool was not uncomfortable. The sounds were pleasant, the rhythm of the two of them on the porch swing and the drone of dry trees and the dozen different chimelike sounds that ring huskily on autumn evenings.

"I like autumn," Carrie said, and then she listened to the crickets. Behind the hills the night wind was getting ready to blow. You could feel its cold intake of breath. Then the wind came up, nipping at the top of their windbreak of pines. "These windy nights you can lie in bed and hear the trees outside busy with dying," Carrie said out of nothing.

"You're very poetic," I said.

It had seemed to need an answer, and yet it didn't. I could feel her smile, though I couldn't see her, and also could feel that Millie was smiling, and after a while we went inside and played cards.

18

The Closing Seasons

IT WAS true about the trees being busy with dying. I listened all the way home from the Littens' that night, and still listened in bed. I heard the jangling and the soft commotion in the flaky, yellowing branches of the hardwoods and all night long there was the stomping of their dance of death, using their last energy to rid themselves of the leaves they had worn so composedly all summer. They shed them like weights too heavy to carry through the winter, and themselves turned to gray sleeping stones, while the night long in the dark wind the cast-off leaves raced from one pocket of the hills to the next, like a band of brown partridges not knowing where to go, or how to find shelter, or provide for themselves, in their new, strange release.

This busyness was in every corner of earth and sky. By October, there were a thousand things the land and marshes and ponds and woods seemed to have been putting off, and must still do before the first snow began with its deceptive, fine-winged flurries. Pods still to burst, sap to sink, tendrils to harden, late fruit to ripen, newts and frogs to bury themselves, birds to catapult themselves southward from the frozen sky of the north. The garden waited to be covered, and hoses to be dragged in, and on the farms the barn-door hinges needed to be repaired and herds brought in and the weatherstripping taped around the attic windows.

What do you do out there all fall and winter? Friends asked it often. There was all this to see and feel, that I hadn't known when I was blown along rainy city streets. Fall came, the earth slept, but now I was a part of it, had found some correlation between myself and a tree. I was not nearly so expendable or little as I had thought. The migrating birds threw chill shadows on the bent, gray meadow grass. No longer did such sights depress me, but lifted me by their mysterious pattern. There was a brief recurrence of summer's excitement when a flock of robins and bluejays, traveling together, alighted on a hillside, scurrying for a noisy instant to feed like a bunch of travelers clucking in pleasant communion around a gas station in a desert—until one bird jerked upward in hasty flight, ten, a hundred, two hundred followed, and a raucous shadow passed over the meadow and rooftop and naked trees and they were gone, leaving behind such silence as if they had carried off with them every material thing on earth able to make sound. The pup Tim, though master now with Shag gone, was suddenly not so sovereign, and raced with loud screams at breakneck speed after the birds as if he were forgotten and was threatened with being left alone on this freezing, barren, food-stripped planet.

But then the ovenbirds came by, and startled me with one of nature's bursts of humor. Because these small birds just kept walking all the time. Up and down the meadow. Back and forth over the floor of the woods. Round and round the terrace, pecking for food in the cracks between the paving stones. Wherever they went, they walked, as if earthbound, or as if someone had forgot to explain to them about wings. And they walked so far, until you would think their feet would burn with exhaustion. Just as I was certain they were going to walk all the way to their southern habitats, they took flight. I watched them go, laughing, and did not feel so forsaken even though they were gone.

*   *   *

That fall meant Walter Cwym came around with his paint brush, which he carried like a badge of his own personal fraternity (sometimes he redecorates his vegetable stand as many as three times a summer, which means his vegetables must rot on the ground—he's too busy to bother picking and selling them), to paint a new arbor and to help repaint the storm windows before they went up. He has appeared every October since as regularly as do the migrating birds, the plumage of his paint buckets as varied.

It also meant more visits from Aunt Dell. She had more time then, the children were in school, her garden had succumbed, died in its prime, a gray mass of tangled stalks and hoar-frosted buds that had struggled to fulfil themselves but seemed to know from the start that they were destined never to bloom, for they gave up at the first hint of frost in the satin-gray dawns. When she has time, Aunt Dell likes to read. She reads for the life in a book, as one should. She thinks all the people in books are real.

"That Mrs. Dodsworth, ainna? Wouldn't you like to wring her in the neck? That nice Sam!"

Her huge heart bled; she was breaking it again, all for nobody. But the people *were* real. The silence and calm let them come alive. In the country that fall before a fire, after I had dug the potatoes and pruned the fruit trees and breathed real air all day, I found time to read the books I always meant to but never found time for before. And I reread old books. I returned to a safe, forgotten land. Faces at first dimly, then with a shock of recognition, reappeared in that landscape. I had lost track of these valuable friends. Madame Chaucat, I thought, as I opened each old volume, are you still rudely slamming doors as you enter the dining room on top the Magic Mountain, and will you love Hans Castorp better this time? Captain Ahab, is the maniac glint as wild as ever in your eye, and are you going to chase the white whale again through northern, southern, western, eastern oceans though I know, and surely you should too, by now, it means only your own tormented death? Anna Karenina, please, don't get off this fateful Petersburg train as it puffs into Moscow. . . . But the train slows down. Blind Anna, just as before, steps from her carriage. There stands Count Vronsky and all unknowingly she gives him her hand. They meet, smile, and her death has begun again.

I lent books to Aunt Dell, and Bud Devere, and the village schoolteacher, and the minister of Jerusalem Church, and borrowed in return. It was like introducing old friends around. Soon everyone knew the same people. They were good people to know, and I missed my city friends less.

*   *   *

During the first despondent winter Jane March lived in the Waldeens' house, I plowed through the snow, carrying an armful of books to her. But she was busy reading something else. Strewn all over the coffee table were the farmers' bulletins and pamphlets sent out by the Department of Agriculture.

"Say, look at these!" Her excitement sparked against the pages. For the first time, the city torpor was absent. "Fix yourself a drink. How are you? Look at all this stuff. Came today in the mail. From Washington. How do you suppose they got sent to me?"

She did not know that I had ordered them sent to her. It had occurred to me that reading these pamphlets might open a way for her, show her a new pattern of orderliness, of continuity, or even a reason for building a new life around her, as they already had done for me.

Her eyes were glittering. I was about to claim her gratitude for having them sent to her, but already she had forgotten to wonder where they came from. "Listen to this!" she went on. "What's a *Rag-Doll Seed Tester*? Does our government really worry with farmers about all these things? Is it that important? About *How to Raise a Pony* and *Carpet and Rug Repairs*? Look, it's like a history of the nation—*Selling Black Walnut Timber*, and then *Modernizing Cotton Gins*, and *Kudzu for Erosion Control in the Southeast*! What's kudzu? God knows I know about erosion—Skip and I saw it down in Alabama—but what's kudzu? And what's dodder? Look, number 1161: *Dodder*. Look at number 1627, like the name of a tragic play: *The Hessian Fly*. All these marvelous words and sounds—well, do all those things about the earth really matter so much?" She was laughing, her cheeks flushed. "How do you like these for a panorama of the country—*Persian Clover* and *Karakul Sheep* and *Mormon Crickets and Their Control*. Sounds as absorbing as a documentary film!"

Reading only the list of titles brought a flush of longing for peace and sanity to Jane's cheeks. And when I had first read them, I too wanted at once to learn about horse bots and wheat smudge, crotalaria culture and sorghum midges—besides the magic compulsion in their names, these became things of infinite importance to know about, once I realized men's lives depended on knowledge of them. A whole, sane, productive world began to seem possible. There was a glow of healthy responsibility in a government that told its farm wives how to make slip covers or bone a lamb cut. *Determining Age of Farm Animals by Their Teeth* made me smile, until I learned how John Hummock, across the road, had been duped into buying for hard cash a stallion too old to rear up on its hind legs.

Farmers love old books, the torn histories, records, albums handed down to them by their ancestors—I learned this from *Preservation of Leather Bookbindings.* A farmer could squint and gauge his earnings, and know his herds were safe for the winter, that in blizzards they would not go hungry, if he read *Measuring Hay in Stacks.* There was drama in *Better Farm Leases.* There was a terrible warning in *When Drought Returns to the Great Plains.*

*   *   *

And that autumn, as I watched the trees busy with dying, was time again for Carrie and Millie to start making roast duck with their secret sauerkraut stuffing, and to put down geese in crocks of goose fat. Buck's mother, Mrs. Fife, baked *bara brieth,* the Welsh holiday cake made with pounds of everything, as if one could not think in smaller quantities, pounds of butter, brown sugar, blue raisins, white raisins, red currants, black currants. Ducks, geese, *bara brieth,* strong and thick soups, these I learned were the concerns of country kitchens, while the men were occupied with playing cards down at the Corners, or repairing their machinery, or repainting the insides of their houses, or taking factory jobs in nearby cities to tide them over—all while windy autumn followed the uncertain road, sometimes ice-coated, sometimes of dismal mud, that led through November and then December to Christmas.

Buck Fife's sister May married her friend Dick, from Genesee, that Christmas Day, and my inclusion in the wedding party (my invited task was not to walk down the aisle with the bridal couple, but to check coats at the dance in a public hall later) made me know that I really lived here, was wanted, now.

Mr. Fife popped in with all his wine from our grapes. There was oldtime dancing, broom dances, in which Aunt Dell always wound up dancing with the broom, and then square-dancing, not by the old people but by the young. I watched their rediscovered joy in dancing the dances of their parents and grandparents, while those elders watched approvingly or sometimes joined in to show them how it was really done, dozens of young couples swaying and turning and circling together, the women in their special long skirts, the men in their special embroidered shirts and high boots. There were a few fights when some of the boys got drunk, brutal flare-ups of anger and strength, and then the raucous confusion of separating the fighting men. Then there were sudden waves of peace again.

The dance lasted late. I drove home tired, I was going home, I had a place on earth. My neighbors liked me, relied on me, expected my help, would help me. I gave them presents, they had given me some. Around me the fields were vast, the hills sheltering, the stars sailing in their icy sea overhead, and clearly this was the Christmas night I had been looking for since I was a child.

Perhaps even better had been the night before, when I was invited to Aunt Dell's house. The presents had all been unwrapped. Tom got a live puppy. Buss was popping ornaments off the tree with a new BB gun. The twins were fighting over identical dolls. Aunt Dell was admiring the new floor lamp she had bought her husband, exactly the kind she wanted. There was coffee cooking violently on the kitchen stove until amid screams Aunt Dell's poor percolator boiled over. A dozen women raced to turn it off, and then there was an unexpected lull.

Neighbors were sitting all around me, looking, waiting— Aunt Dell, in a fit of luck, had even been able to drag a few strangers home from church, to fill the odd corners of her huge, cluttery parlor. Outside the windows, the hills were a flowing, moonlit blue, and the town street like a long wide river of snow. Then without preamble, after the momentary lull, Aunt Dell started telling the stories of her childhood in the cabin that stood in these woods half a century ago, picking up a narrative thread she had dropped the Christmas before as if there had been no intermission. They made a kind of chronicle. She recalled the stories almost haphazardly at first, goaded by relatives or the children, playing one memory unsentimentally against another, even with huge laughter, until the whole evolved like a kind of abundant, marvelous singing from Aunt Dell's lungs. She sighed heavily, and just in time, it seemed, rescued her stories again from oblivion.

She burst into satisfied laughter, remembering the log cabin of no more than two rooms. In it lived fourteen children, one of them herself, and her mother and father. Her father had bought the land unseen, and only when they arrived there did he discover what he had bought—acres of uncleared land, tall trees, and rocks. But they still had Christmas in the crowded two rooms. They had homemade candles on a tree and ornaments of nuts and prunes wrapped in bits of colored paper that had been saved all year long.

"And tell about where the tree hung!" the children cried.

"From the ceiling, ainna?" Aunt Dell answered, as if even she disbelieved it. "On the floor, with all us kids, there wasn't room. So why shouldn't we hang it from the ceiling? It swung back and forth—" her voice grew grander "—rather pretty."

"The presents," Tom prompted with a gentle nod.

"We didn't get presents by the galore like you kiddoes," she said quietly. "Pa was poor, and even feeding us kiddoes was a job, wasn't it? But he and Ma never forgot. One thing there was always for each of us. The pencil box. Or a jumpingjack. Or Annie's gold hairpins, ainna?"

"Tell about the time you all died, Ma," Buss said cheerfully.

This was the favorite story, of Annie and the gold hairpins, and the year of black diphtheria. Aunt Dell told it carefully, seeming to shrink in size, while neighbors listened with clucking nods and the children half in fear. How one of the brothers went to help a neighbor tend a sick cow. How sickness must have been in that barn. How the brother quickly fell ill, how the fever spread then from child to child. Until in a week's time five of the brothers and sisters died. How Pa sat at a table day and night, like a frozen crane on a chair, looking down at his hands, as if all this slaughter were his doing. How the doctor from the nearest city thirty miles away finally came, a young man just beginning practice, and when he diagnosed the disease and knew what he had to fight, broke down weeping and had to be steadied back to reality and action by Ma. How one of the children (who must have been Aunt Dell), not yet infected, sat by the cabin's single frosted window, doing nothing especially, blowing on the pane and erasing the frozen ferns and miniature crystal forests from the glass to make a tiny peephole through which she watched all day, for nothing, especially, only watching.

"Hurry up, Ma," Tom said, still gentle. "Tell about Annie and her gold hair."

Annie, one of the sisters, was in her early teens and had golden hair so long she could sit on the braids. It was her wildest joy. Her single present that Christmas before the fever had been a finer one than she had ever dreamed of. Pa gave it to her, and he must have been a thoughtful man. He had brought it back with him from the city, when he went down by horse and wagon for the winter's supply of food and clothing. It was a five-cent package of gilt hairpins, palely lustrous as was her hair.

Annie treasured them so, like a gold crown for her hair, that she hid them. None of her brothers and sisters could ever find them, try to pilfer them from her as they might. Until she was dying, the winter of the fever. Then she told her sisters to bring them to her from their hiding place, in the horsehair stuffing of the sofa, and one by one doled them out to them, leaving behind her the best gift she had.

Some of the old neighbors in the room remembered this story from when it happened. They had lived here then, too.

"You still got the hairpins she gave you?" Buss demanded suspiciously of his mother.

"Nope, smarty. Lost 'em, long ago," Aunt Dell said.

Everyone laughed then, the old neighbors, remembering the past, and Aunt Dell as heartily as any, until suddenly all the laughter died away, and for half an instant there was no sound whatever.

*   *   *

But Aunt Dell's stories recalled another Christmas, nearer in time, and the remarkable events of an evening when I was twelve. It was because the pastor of our small church, John Thomas, was among the crowd in Aunt Dell's parlor, a quiet man, enormously kind, with pale, blinking eyes sunk deep in his long face. And he reminded me of the pastor that night when I was twelve. It was a good story to remember in the country, because I felt closer to it now, here with these faces that looked more like boyhood's faces, laughing, less frightening, with the familiar smells of coffee cooking and candles burning. But I had forgotten it until I saw John's face, there like the spirit of the other minister, merging yesteryear and today.

I watched young Tom Dell too, and wondered if this was the boy I was on that night. It could have been. He is adventurous, foolhardly sometimes, dreamy, biting off more than he can swallow, and I watched Aunt Dell's eyes held on him in wise understanding and they were not unlike the eyes out of which my parents must have gazed that night.

Our pastor in a small upstate town, where we lived for a year—the old pastor, Reverend Nagel—must have had that understanding, too, even as I could also see it now on John Thomas' long face, as it leaned in sober, kindly chatter over the youngest of Aunt Dell's brood, the twins. Our church, when I was the boy young Tom is now, was going to have a Christmas Eve entertainment, the usual speaking of pieces and choral singing. But why shouldn't it be something grander, why not a spectacle to awe the congregation of the tiny Lutheran church? And why shouldn't the boy of twelve devise, act in, and direct this marvelous pageant? Reverend Nagel, blinking his deep-sunken eyes, listened thoughtfully with the respect he might have given a man his own age (as John Thomas was listening now to the twins' arguments over their identical dolls). And then Reverend Nagel not only gave his permission but his blessing in a rash, if Christian, way, that must have made the recording angels put a star of uncommon size after his name.

It didn't faze me in the least that I couldn't get any of the other boys in the town to take part in our play. I simply assigned the roles of both a shepherd and a wise man to myself. As a matter of fact, I played *all* the shepherds and wise men. Our church was poor, and there was the matter of costumes, but that was no real problem either. As the shepherds, I could wear my wool bathrobe, which was flowing and rich. That it was covered with bright orange and green Navajo Indian designs was nothing to worry a boy. And for my role as the wise men I could simply add a gold paper crown.

I was to appear first as the shepherds, marching down the narrow aisle, singing "O Little Town of Bethlehem" as I moved toward the altar, where the girls of the Sunday School classes would enact a Nativity tableau, complete with virgin, child in manger, and angels bewinged in cheesecloth, none over the age of ten. Then after I had knelt to deposit my shepherds' gift of a stuffed lamb that belonged to my sister, I would disappear behind the altar, out through the back door of the church, race around outside to the front vestibule, put on my crown, and march down the aisle again, this time singing "We Three Kings of Orient Are" and bearing gifts of frankincense and myrrh.

I didn't know what myrrh was, but my mother had a pretty incense burner in the shape of a naked dancing woman carrying what looked like a clothes hamper on her head. I figured I could use that for the frankincense. Myrrh, the dictionary said, was a gummy resin. I borrowed the resin with which my father used to wax his fiddle bow, though it seemed a nonsensical gift to be handing a newborn babe. As a final, stupendous theatrical touch, I had rigged up a wire the length of the church aisle and a sliding electric star. Someone hidden in the balcony would guide the star along the wire and I would reverently follow it down the aisle to the manger. It was something to stir a boy's imagination. Grain by grain I would feel the cool desert sand under my bare feet (which in reality were shod, because my mother wouldn't let me go running barefoot through the snow outside the church as I switched roles) while I trailed the bright beckoning star to the humble stable.

That night when I saw John Thomas at Aunt Dell's house I had begun blushing furiously, and without knowing why, but that moment was also the first time in years I had recalled what happened when Christmas Eve finally came. I began my shepherds' pilgrimage down the aisle, but I had forgotten to bring my sister's stuffed lamb and so I went empty-handed. Nevertheless, I sang with gusto, in time to my slow, worshipful footsteps. Then raced around outside (being careful not to get my new shoes spotted in the snow) to start on my second trip down the aisle as the wise men. Only, someone had misplaced my gold crown, frankincense and myrrh in the front vestibule, or else had piled coats and tasselcaps over it, and though I hunted like Herod's soldiers for the Innocents I couldn't find them, and so had to go empty-handed down the aisle again.

This time I was scared, and my voice failed me, and the organist waited for me to start singing but since I didn't begin, she didn't start playing the pump organ, because the bellows didn't work too well and she was conserving air, so I just walked in silence, leaving the congregation a little confused as to the plot because all they saw was a boy who just kept walking down the aisle in his bathrobe. Around the altar a bunch of angels tittered with less-than-angelic, nervous pleasure. But what was worse, the star got jittery. Or rather, the boy in the balcony working it did, and just before I started down toward the manger on my second trip, he let the star slip by mistake, and it zoomed like a comet past me, at such a speed that I couldn't have followed it on my bike. He started to haul it back again, so he could do it over properly, but I was already on my way. So that while I went down the aisle, my guiding star slowly crawled *up* the aisle, and we passed, as it were, in mid-desert.

But after church Reverend Nagel, gently blinking his pallid eyes, told me how nice the show had been. With thoughtful deliberation, he admired my skill in facial expressions. I think I believed him until I was out of church and on the cold town streets alone. Too clearly I could see the jocose girl-angels and the stunned congregation and my parents sitting with frozen, if crimson, faces and the mystifying film on my mother's eyes. I started the few blocks home, and looked up at the brilliant sky that was supposed to be heraldic with joy, but all I saw was a lot of stars that seemed to float backwards, and I suppose I considered running away, but after an hour of wandering I climbed the stairs to home.

They were waiting for me to start celebrating Christmas. And no one even asked why I was so late. One of my presents was to have been a new bathrobe and tactfully my mother put this away, and did not bring it out again for several weeks when, one day, I just found it hanging in my closet. And Reverend Nagel, I remember, came over to our house that night, near midnight, surprising everybody, just as we were finishing Christmas, and stayed to drink coffee and eat frosted stollen with us and once or twice to smile at me again, as if in blinking, recollected admiration of my facial expressions.

At Aunt Dell's house, when I saw John Thomas' long, pale face and this boy of twelve came back to me, all mixed up with young Tom and Aunt Dell's wise eyes, I think I must have let myself grow abstracted. Because John was tapping my shoulder.

"I've been saying, it's nice to have you here with us." His eyes blinked. In other men, it might have been a grin. "We're always glad to welcome any stranger who moves in among us."

I couldn't tell him we weren't strangers.

19

More Magi

W E CAN'T do any shopping for presents this year," Millie had said that same Christmas, "what with the Essex laid up."

I hadn't known there was anything wrong with their car, and offered to drive them into town the next day. I would pick them up around noon.

"Oh, you needn't bother. We'll drive over as far as your place," Carrie said. "Saves you a trip."

So how was the Essex "laid up"? They just wanted company, that's all. But I was glad to drive them in, rather than go in with them in their car, because I knew how they felt about alcohol. They are convinced it will ignite and explode if placed in a radiator, and have never been persuaded to use it. So after they've used the Essex on a winter day, they drive it into their barn; Millie, as adept with petcocks as a high-school boy, drains the radiator, and the hood is covered with a half-dozen blankets like a horse. When they want to take another cruise, they emerge from the house with steaming teakettles and pails of boiling water and the Essex starts like a dream. But this was a messy procedure to go through, parked on the Five Points in Waukesha, when they went in for their shopping. Though they do not hesitate to swing wide the petcocks even there on the main street, drain the radiator, and later borrow pails and cans and kettles of hot water from every shop along the block to start their car up again.

We were having days of zero weather. They reached my house promptly at noon, still having refused to let me pick them up—I think it was a matter of courtesy to them that they come at least part way. The petcocks were opened, the hood of the Essex draped, and they climbed into my car, both in the seat beside me. It was a little the feeling of double vision, because they were wearing identical hats, a solution, Carrie explained cheerfully, to their habit of wearing each other's hat by mistake. This way they wouldn't look peculiar, in case they did.

"We shouldn't be dawdling," Carrie said, when I purposely held the car back because I thought winter driving might frighten them. "We've got a lot of shopping to do."

I asked what they meant to shop for.

"Etceteras," Millie said.

The first etcetera, after we pulled up at the Five Points, turned out to be ice-cream sodas. I think Dollie, the cop, saw us arrive, because he left his traffic post in the middle of the five-way intersection and walked off in the opposite direction from us, not rapidly but inexorably, and marched straight into the women's hosiery store on the corner, not even glancing back when a pair of fenders clanged against each other behind him. All the cars were like unfenced cows coming in five directions, and I got Millie and Carrie into the drugstore as fast as I could. We had sodas, and there was some quick-change work again. I paid for them, leaving a tip, which Carrie absently picked up and put into her purse. Then Millie opened her purse and insisted they always paid their own way, handing me the price of their two sodas in substantiation of it, nine cents shy, and Carrie looked at me and said, "Ought to leave a tip for these girls. They work hard," and her gaze was so imploring that I put down another dime. Carrie looked disappointed so I changed it to a quarter which Millie must have misunderstood to be her change for the change she had given me for their sodas, because she picked it up and put it in her purse. Somehow, I was fourteen cents out.

"All settled?" Carrie smiled impatiently.

I nodded. "We'd better get going."

"We certainly had, unless we want to miss the newsreel," Carrie said.

Etceteras, I learned then, also included going to a movie, after which we really had to hurry to finish their shopping in the hour or so that remained before closing time. I don't know how in that time we made eight or nine stores. Our first stop was the women's-wear department of one of the big stores, where Carrie asked to see some of "their best garments" and boldly, in front of me, minutely and with a critical pursing of her lips, examined the workmanship, seams, insertions, and crotches of some astoundingly expensive pieces of underwear certainly not intended to be worn by her. Her final judgment on them, however, was one of satisfaction and even of praise as she handed them back to the clerk in a heap of mild disorder for her to put back in their boxes. In the meanwhile, Millie had sauntered into the toy department among the electric trains. There was one already set up and operating, and she watched fascinatedly, with a rhythmical careening of her head, as the train went round and round on its track, switching to nowhere and going around some more. Then she asked the clerk to see a more elaborate

set and watched patiently while he set it up, and showed rapt
interest as he demonstrated a logging car hauling real logs,
and next such other appurtenances as drawbridges, gates, a cattle car that loaded itself and then got unloaded, and finally a
miniature switchman who kept jigging out and flagging the
train, which seemed to depress her, after which she shook
hands with the clerk, thanked him, tipped him a nickel, and
walked away.

By this time Miss Carrie was beginning to smell pretty high.
She was in the cosmetics department, being sprayed with old-
fashioned "Sweet Pea." She waved a hand testily when the clerk
brought out the fancy names, like "Fleurs des Rocailles." Every
once in a while the clerk would look at her hat and then see
another one just like it bobbing around somewhere in the
crowd, and then she would look at Carrie reflectively. Millie
finally joined Carrie and was sprayed, too, after which we
started off across the street to a sporting-goods store which,
from their nervous fidgeting and pinched cheeks, they might
have expected to find as crammed with naked men as a locker
room. Millie gingerly inquired about an assortment of equipment, mitts, clubs, bats, for their nephew who had not, so far
as I know, existed until that moment. It set me to wondering
what children of their own would have meant to them, and I
began thinking about Millie's annual aborted wedding trip,
but by then they had discovered a rack of guns and their absorption in a Belgian over-and-under gun, priced at eight hundred dollars, made it clear that the nephew had already been
sent back to limbo. They are both good markswomen and their
intelligent discussion of the gun's merits with the clerk, and the
sure way Carrie hoisted the gun experimentally to her shoulder,
made me recall their terror during the time of the mail-pouch
robbery, and how rigidly they perhaps still lay beside each other

in bed at night at sound of a prowling footstep outside. It would have made anyone long to be able to buy the expensive gun for them and make their nights peaceful, but by then they had come across a display of fishing tackle, shotguns and safety were forgotten, and they were laughing together over some minnows that glowed, senselessly it seemed to them, in the dark.

After a while they again thanked the clerk politely, and then we went to an appliance store and watched TV for a while. In the five-and-ten, they actually did make a purchase—one Christmas card. (They asked me to help pick it out, and two days later I got it in the mail, though unsigned.) At the next stop in a furniture store, they had a clerk open up several sofa-beds for them to poke the mattresses, and then Carrie went around and lit all the table lamps on display. One didn't have a bulb and she waited until the clerk unscrewed one from another lamp and put it in the empty socket, whereupon she nodded, satisfied, and we left. There were still two minutes remaining before closing time, but suddenly they wanted to go home.

"What about all the shopping you were going to do? You didn't buy a thing," I said.

They looked pale and tired, and they ignored my question, and climbed in to settle comfortably on the car seat. They smiled at each other with the look of a day that, if exhausting, was at any rate well spent.

"Gives you a real oldtime holiday spirit, doesn't it?" Carrie asked.

I suppose it did, because several times on the way home I caught them humming a carol. It was a peculiar sensation. Because each time I glanced at them, they were dozing, and neither could have been singing. But I swear I heard it.

20

Waldeen

NEAR home both Millie and Carrie were abruptly alert as we passed the Waldeens' house, which had stood abandoned since the end of summer. Ed and Paulie had never come back home again after they went away that last August on their final, stupendous journey. A few times more, as the drought lingered on into autumn, I had gone up to water the flowering trees Paulie had set out that spring, and once or twice I found other neighbors, with the same idea of saving Paulie's trees for her, had already been there before me, and the trees prospered in moist earth. But everyone kept waiting for them to come back. Instead, they went on their remarkable trip and then Paulie went directly into a hospital. She had wanted to keep singing the song of life as long as possible, I suppose with the idea that it was such a marvelous song while it lasted.

Winter made their house look as if it had been unlived in much longer than it had. Automatically I drove faster, to get past it. At that time, no one knew yet that Paulie was in the hospital a hundred or so miles away. "I wonder when they'll be coming back home. They're staying away such a long time," I said.

"They're not coming back," Carrie said.

"Why wouldn't they? What do you mean?"

Both Carrie and Millie looked stronger and more formidable —I had seen this look once before in a country woman, in Aunt Dell, when she had gazed toward the Waldeens' house and rebelled against the senselessness of life and its patterns. Even Millie's frail body went to steel, and Carrie's plumper shape was resolute as the stone wall along Ed Waldeen's fields.

"Paulie's dying. It's why she went away," Millie said. "She won't come back."

"How do you know?"

The two pairs of shoulders, one thin, one stout, shrugged. But they knew, however they knew it. They sat there looking silent and wise and old and compassionate as the hills and snow-covered meadows we sped by, as much a part of the earth as these were, as right and indestructible a part of it as the chill air we breathed and the wind that raced after us. And what they knew, they knew. And were right, of course.

"Dying's not so much," Carrie said with a soft laugh, almost shy again. "Enough do that before they grow up and still keep walking around. But that little Paulie. She was different. She liked it here."

"Here? Where's here?"

"*Here!*" Carrie snapped.

I looked around. Everywhere was here, was what Carrie meant. That was it. That was my ultimate lesson, the answer to all the questions I had asked again and again that one trapped, despairing winter. *Here* was Earth. *Here* to Paulie, with her fragile babushka-framed face and flutey but meaningful voice, was being alive, loving Ed, her boundlessness, freedom, loving fog, hills, pastures, the sun commanding things to grow, her piano, her neighbors, every single experience. The death was not important, or anything they could fight, but what happened until that utter instant was, and so she and Ed, because each knew and because each was what the other loved most, had shut out everyone else to live together as long and fully as they could.

That was why they shut their doors, after the big farewell party which no one knew was a farewell. That made their sign: KEEP OUT. It was not unfriendly, after all. Then they went on their last, sad trip, traveling the way they liked, in good hotels, eating fine things, seeing sights, like any lovesick pair on their first trip, defying, appreciating, big strapping Ed, little Paulie, and when it was plain that the cancer was in its final stages they took a train back to the hospital, where they were expected (where, though no one knew it, Paulie had already undergone one operation a year before, when all their neighbors thought they were gone on a fishing trip) and where Paulie died before spring came again.

Ed came back only long enough to get rid of their place. It seemed everything he loved, and Paulie loved, everything all of us loves, he wanted to get rid of. He looked glum and drawn, and old with a kind of terror the way he had looked that one afternoon up on the hillside beside the fire, and he packed up a few bags of belongings, and condemned himself to the city, as if without Paulie the things he loved couldn't have any meaning. But all of his neighbors are certain that someday he will have to come back.

In the meantime, in the years since Jane March has been living in the Waldeen place, the trees that Paulie planted, knowing she would never see them bloom, have grown to

blooming size. Those trees explain the story of Paulie Waldeen.
Look at them—you seem to hear a song of the land, a word repeated again and again, *life, life, life.* . . .

*   *   *

I think of Paulie, the trees, J.R.'s ad in our paper, the women
of Verdi Square, a dozen other things combining together,
every year as spring comes around. I thought of them the spring
when Jane was going to marry me. Thinking how much all the
good things had come to mean—earth, sky, time, space, air,
silence—sent me wandering through the woods to the hills, to
the highest, to look around at the stretching view, but in which,
on this strange, unexpectedly still day, no living thing was stirring—no neighbor plowing his field, no cattle grazing new
grass, no car on the highway, only more hills, trees, sky. Occasionally a tower of smoke said a train was passing by. But that
floated away and was soon forgotten. There was no life but that
of the earth itself, the intensifying sunlight, a chipmunk, mosses
underfoot. I began to think of J.R.'s panic. I felt a panicky
need of my own to cry out: Where is Man?

The sun clouded over. Behind the hills, there was a sudden
sharp glimmer of light. As quickly, it was gone. What if, when
I came down the hill in search of friends and neighbors, I could
find no one? No Jane March waiting to marry me, or Aunt Dell,
no Bud Devere, no Carrie or Millie or Walter Cwym, no Hummocks, no Fifes? What if all Time were wasted? What if I had
not yet been alive, and now was alone? What if, as J.R. feared,
I had lost the world?

Suddenly, everything was destruction. Everything was gone.
There was a surge of power because all the earth's riches, its
possessions, were mine. All the houses, all the cars, all the rail-
roads and ships to travel where I want, all the money, all the

books, the secrets. But what good would they do me, alone? Aunt Dell's house was crushed by boulders, the fields that John Hummock and Buck Fife and Ed Waldeen used to plough were gray, misty dust. The trees were without leaf, the barns were ashes, the herds lay still. There was only one comfort. I had lost everything, but at least I had learned to know and love what I lost.

In the distant sky was another flash, far brighter, far whiter, though it was only lightning. But it scared my fox from his far hill and he flew by me, still racing for his freedom. Then the same paralyzing fear sent me racing down the hill toward Jane's house.

And on the lawn the trees were blooming a reassuring pink and white. And I lived on earth. It was spring everywhere. Inside, Jane was waiting. And then I could hear Paulie's song again, the voice of the land, *life, life, life.* . . .

About the Author

Edward Harris Heth was born in Wisconsin and attended the University of Wisconsin. His first short story, written in college, was bought by H. L. Mencken for *The American Mercury* in 1930. Writing became Heth's career, and he produced seven novels, one of which, *Any Number Can Play*, ranks among the best gambling stories ever written.

Heth lived in New York City for several years. When movie rights to *Any Number Can Play* were sold, he returned to Wisconsin, where he built a spacious home—the House on the Hill—in the rural area between Wales and Dousman. Soon sketches and stories describing Heth's rambles across the countryside and his engaging encounters with his neighbors began to appear in local weekly newspapers. Some of the characters were so loved and the fan mail about them so great that *My Life on Earth* was published in 1953. Though it is not autobiography except in the freest sense, its scenes are pure Wisconsin. Heth's deep, gentle affection for the countryside and its people—he admitted that writing the book gave him more pleasure than any other work he had done—makes *My Life on Earth* a warm and unforgettable book.

A brilliant amateur cook and gardener, Heth wrote *The Wonderful World of Cooking*, a unique combination of recipes and country wisdom, in 1956. It was to be his last book. The House on the Hill was struck by lightning and burned in 1960, and Heth died suddenly in Milwaukee in 1963, leaving an unfinished novel. Heth never considered himself a regional writer, believing that "a writer is either good or bad, and that's all." It is a tribute to his excellence that his works, strong in Wisconsin atmosphere, transcend the region and have national appeal.

C78262

S521
H478   Heth, Edward Harris.
            My life on earth. Illus. by Edwin Schmidt.
        Madison, Wis., Wisconsin Tales and Trails,
        1973, [c1953]
            247 p. illus.

            1. Country life—Wisconsin. I. Title.